BTEC FIRST

REVISE BTEC

Health and Social Care

Unit 1 Human Lifespan Development

Unit 9 Healthy Living

REVISION WORKBOOK

Series Consultant: Harry Smith

Authors: Brenda Baker and Elizabeth Haworth

THE REVISE BTEC SERIES

BTEC First in Health and Social Care Revision Guide
9781446909812

BTEC First in Health and Social Care Revision Workbook
9781446909829

This Workbook is designed to complement your classroom and home learning, and to help prepare you for the test. It does not include all the content and skills needed for the complete course. It is designed to work in combination with Pearson's main BTEC First series.

To find out more visit:
www.pearsonschools.co.uk/revise

ALWAYS LEARNING

PEARSON

Published by Pearson Education Limited, Edinburgh Gate, Harlow, Essex, CM20 2JE.

www.pearsonschoolsandfecolleges.co.uk

Copies of official specifications for all Pearson qualifications may be found on the website: www.edexcel.com

Text © Pearson Education Limited 2014
Typeset by Tech-Set Ltd, Gateshead
Original illustrations © Pearson Education Limited
Cover photo/illustration by Miriam Sturdee

The rights of Brenda Baker and Elizabeth Haworth to be identified as authors of this work have been asserted by them in accordance with the Copyright, Designs and Patents Act 1988.

First published 2014

17 16 15 14
10 9 8 7 6 5 4 3 2 1

British Library Cataloguing in Publication Data
A catalogue record for this book is available from the British Library

ISBN 978 1 4469 0982 9

Printed in Slovakia by Neografia

Picture Credits

The publisher would like to thank the following for their kind permission to reproduce their photographs:
(Key: b-bottom; c-centre; l-left; r-right; t-top)

Corbis: Tanya Constantine / Blend Images 11tr, Tetra Images 7tr; **Pearson Education Ltd:** Jules Selmes 20tr, 80br; **Shutterstock.com:** Robert Kneschke 33tr; **Veer / Corbis:** Evgenyatamanenko 5br, iofoto 19tr, Steven Frame 1cr
All other images © Pearson Education

Picture Research by: Susie Prescott

Every effort has been made to trace the copyright holders and we apologise in advance for any unintentional omissions. We would be pleased to insert the appropriate acknowledgement in any subsequent edition of this publication..

The author and publisher would like to thank the following organisation for their approval and permission to produce their materials:

p40 Definition of 'health': Preamble to the Constitution of the World Health Organization as adopted by the International Health Conference, New York, 19-22 June, 1946; signed on 22 July 1946 by the representatives of 61 States (Official Records of the World Health Organization, no. 2, p. 100) and entered into force on 7 April 1948. The Definition has not been amended since 1948.

Contents

This book covers the externally assessed units in the BTEC Level 1/Level 2 First in Health and Social Care qualification.

- -

 These questions provide part of a model answer to help you get started.

Pearson publishes Sample Assessment Material and the Specification on its website. That is the official content, and this book should be used in conjunction with it. The questions in this book have been written to help you practise what you have learned in your revision. Remember: the real test questions may not look like this.

The six life stages

1   The following information is about the Brookes family.
Read the information and answer the questions below.

> Paul is 48 years old. He is married to Sara who is 35.
> They have two children, Ruby aged 4 and Millie aged 2.

> Make sure you learn the names of the life stages and their age boundaries.

⟩ **Guided** ⟩

(a) Identify a member of the family who is in the early childhood life stage and a member of the family who is in the early adulthood life stage.

(2 marks)

1. Ruby is in the early childhood life stage

2. ....

> This is Sara's mother, Trudie. She is 66 years old.

(b) What is Trudie's current life stage?   (1 mark)

Put a cross in **one** box ☒ to indicate your answer.

A ☐ Adolescence

B ☐ Early adulthood

C ☐ Middle adulthood

D ☐ Later adulthood

> If you change your mind, put a line through the box and then put a cross in another box.

(c) Give the age range of the adolescence life stage.   (1 mark)

....

Aspects of development

1   The following information is about the Ahmed family.
Read the information and answer the questions below.

> Salma is 30 and is married to Adesh. Adesh's father, Chetan, is 69 and has lived with them since his wife died last year. The death of his wife has affected Chetan's emotional development.

▷ **Guided** ▷   **(a)** Define the term 'emotional development'.   **(1 mark)**

Emotional development is the development of feelings about ....

....

> Adesh has noticed that Chetan is not remembering things as well as he used to.

(b) Identify the aspect of development that is **most** affected by Chetan's memory loss.   **(1 mark)**

....

....

> There is no need to write a whole sentence. You only need to **identify** the aspect of development.

> During his spare time, Adesh enjoys playing cricket for his local team. Salma has just started a language course in the evening.

(c) Identify the aspects of Adesh and Salma's development that are **most** supported by their hobbies.   **(2 marks)**

Draw lines to match the hobbies to the aspect of development.

Hobby	Aspect of development
	Physical
Playing cricket	Intellectual
	Emotional
Studying a language	Social

Growth and physiological change

1   The following information is about the Clarke family.
Read the information and answer the questions below.

> Jane is 54 years old. She has two children, Reece aged 19 and Toby aged 15. Jane's father Bill, who is 78, lives with them.

Guided   **(a)** Outline the difference between 'growth' and 'physiological' change.   **(2 marks)**

Growth is an increase in size, such as height, ...

.... Growth can be measured.

Physiological change is a ....

....

(b) Identify **one** physical or physiological development that each member of the family is likely to be experiencing at their life stage.   **(4 marks)**

Draw lines to match each person to their likely physical or physiological development.

Names	Physical/physiological development
Jane	Has reached physical maturity
Reece	Has lost some muscle tone
Toby	Is experiencing a growth spurt
Bill	Has started the menopause

> Start by identifying the life stage of each person in the family. This will help you to match the person to the physical or physiological change they may be experiencing.

3

Gross motor skills

1   The following information is about the children in the White family.
Read the information and answer the questions below.

> There are three children in the White family: Aidan aged 8, Lana aged 4, and Cory who is 12 months. Aidan and Lana go to school, but Cory is looked after at home by his dad, Daniel.

(a) Give **two** examples of gross motor skills that Lana is developing at this life stage.   **(2 marks)**

1. ....

....

2. ....

....

> Daniel wants to help Cory develop his gross motor skills.

(b) Give **two** examples of activities that could help Cory develop his gross motor skills at this life stage.   **(2 marks)**

1. ....

....

2. ....

....

> Aidan enjoys playing outside in the garden. He has lots of space to run around in and he has a climbing frame and trampoline.

Guided

(c) Explain **two** positive effects of playing in the garden on Aidan's gross motor skills.   **(4 marks)**

1. Climbing on the frame will strengthen the muscles in Aidan's ....

.... because ....

2. Aidan will develop coordination when bouncing on the trampoline because he will need to

use ....

Fine motor skills

1   The following information is about Duncan.
Read the information and answer the questions below.

> Duncan is 18 months old. He is developing his fine and gross motor skills.

> Guided

(a) Outline the difference between fine motor skills and gross motor skills.   **(2 marks)**

Fine motor skills are skills needed to control the .... muscles in the ....

....

Gross motor skills are skills needed to control the ....

in the ....

(b) Which **two** activities are most effective in developing fine motor skills?   **(2 marks)**

Put a cross in **two** boxes ☒ to indicate your answer.

A ☐ Kicking a ball

B ☐ Finger painting

C ☐ Swinging

D ☐ Feeding self

E ☐ Jumping

> Duncan likes building towers with blocks.

(c) Give **two** examples of fine motor skills that Duncan may develop when building with blocks.   **(2 marks)**

1. ....

....

....

2. ....

....

....

There are a number of different fine motor skills. In this question, remember to think only about those that Duncan will need when he is picking up the blocks and putting them on top of each other.

Physical development in adolescence

1   The following information is about Patryk and his sister Maria.
Read the information and answer the questions below.

> Patryk is 15 years old and his sister Maria is 13. Patryk has recently experienced a growth spurt and physical changes in his body.

> **Guided**

(a) Define the term 'growth spurt'. **(1 mark)**

A growth spurt is when a young person grows more

quickly than ....

....

> When you are asked to **define** a term, imagine you are explaining it to someone who knows nothing about the topic.

(b) In which of the following age ranges is Patryk **most** likely to reach physical maturity?

(1 mark)

Put a cross in **one** box ☒ to indicate your answer.

A ☐   From 10 to 12

B ☐   From 14 to 16

C ☐   From 18 to 20

D ☐   From 24 to 26

(c) Give **two** examples of changes to primary sexual characteristics that Maria will experience at her life stage. **(2 marks)**

1. ....

....

2. ....

....

(d) Give **two** examples of secondary sexual characteristics that Maria will develop at her life stage.

(2 marks)

1. ....

....

2. ....

....

Physical development in adulthood

1   The following information is about Robert and his daughter Lily. Read the information and answer the questions below.

> Robert is 77 years of age. He has a daughter, Lily, who is 52.
>
> Lily has just started going through the menopause.

(a) Give **two** examples of the physical or physiological changes that Lily may experience during the menopause. **(2 marks)**

1.   ....
    ....

2.   ....
    ....

> Robert has always enjoyed gardening, but has recently had to give it up.

⟩ Guided ⟩   (b) Explain **two** physical factors related to Robert's life stage that may make gardening difficult.
(4 marks)

1.   Robert may find that moving and bending down to garden is more difficult because
    ....
    ....

2.   Robert may find that he has less strength because ....
    ....
    ....

Intellectual development

1   The following information is about Ray.
Read the information and answer the questions below.

> Ray is 69 years old. He enjoys watching TV quizzes, but is starting to find it more difficult to answer the questions.

(a) Give **two** possible reasons why Ray may be finding it difficult to answer the quiz questions.
(2 marks)

1. ....

2. ....

(b) Give **two** examples of activities that could be used to promote Ray's intellectual development.
(2 marks)

1. ....

2. ....

> Guided

2   The following information is about Caden.
Read the information and answer the questions below.

> Caden is 10 years old. He is currently at primary school, but he is looking forward to going to secondary school next term.

Assess how Caden's intellectual development at his life stage will help him cope with the level of work required at secondary school.
(8 marks)

Caden should have developed a wide vocabulary. This will help him to ....

....

....

Caden will have developed skills to help him to think creatively and use abstract thought

processes. These skills will help him to ....

....

When Caden is given maths tasks to work out, he will be able to use his ....

to help him to work out the answers. He should have well-developed memory and recall skills.

These are important for ....

....

Language development

1 The following information is about the Wilson-Hancock family.
Read the information and answer the questions below.

> There are four children in the Wilson-Hancock family: Noah aged 8, Ryan aged 3, Chloe aged 2, and Maggie, who is 6 months.

> You need to know how language develops for children at different ages within the life stages.

(a) (i) Draw lines to match each child to the description that best describes their language development. **(4 marks)**

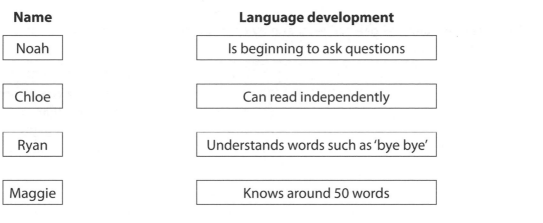

Name	Language development
Noah	Is beginning to ask questions
Chloe	Can read independently
Ryan	Understands words such as 'bye bye'
Maggie	Knows around 50 words

(ii) Give **two** examples of activities that could be used to develop Chloe's language skills at her life stage. **(2 marks)**

1. ....

....

2. ....

....

> Ryan has just started nursery.

Guided

(b) Explain **two** possible effects of starting nursery on Ryan's language development. **(4 marks)**

1. Playing with other children will help Ryan to develop his ....

and .... skills.

2. Listening to stories and rhymes will help Ryan to develop and extend his ....

Moral development

1 The following information is about the Kubiak family.
Read the information and answer the questions below.

> Josep and Ania have one child, Milek, who is 4 years old. Milek still finds it difficult to take turns and share. Josep and Ania want to encourage his moral development.

(a) Define the term 'moral development'. **(1 mark)**

....

....

(b) Give **two** examples of activities that may promote Milek's moral development at his life stage.
(2 marks)

1. ....

....

....

> Think about activities suitable for young children that encourage sharing and taking turns.

2. ....

....

 **(c)** Explain **one** reason why adolescents may hold different moral values to their parents.
(2 marks)

Adolescents are developing ....

.... and are therefore beginning

to question the moral values of others.

Emotional development

1 The following information is about Lucy.
   Read the information and answer the question below.

> Lucy is 15 years old. She is showing photos to her friends. She enjoys being with them, but she sometimes worries about what her friends think of her.

Give **one** possible reason why Lucy may have a positive self-image and **one** possible reason why Lucy may have a negative self-image.

(2 marks)

Positive ....

....

Negative ....

....

> Remember that self-image is about how we see ourselves. This can be influenced by comparison with others or comments made by others.

2 The following information is about Natalie and Mark.
   Read the information and answer the questions below.

> Natalie is 34. She has been dating Mark, aged 30, for the last year. Last month they got married and moved into their new house. Natalie has a good job in a bank. Mark works as a mechanic.

Guided

(a) Explain **two** possible effects of getting married on Natalie's emotional development.

(4 marks)

1. Natalie may have high self-esteem because she is ....

....

2. Natalie may feel more secure because ....

....

> Recently, Mark was made redundant from his job.

(b) Explain **two** possible effects of being made redundant on Mark's emotional development.

(4 marks)

1. ....

....

2. ....

....

Social development

1   The following information is about the Sharma family.
Read the information and answer the questions below.

> Yasir, aged 47, is happily married to Maya, who is 39. They have one son, Deepak, who is 15 years old. Deepak is developing his independence.

Guided

(a) Define the term 'independence'.   **(1 mark)**

Independence is being able to make your own decisions, ...

.... and ....

....

> Yasir works full time. Maya does not work, but she is studying a language at college.

(b) Describe **two** possible effects of attending college on Maya's social development.   **(4 marks)**

1. ....

....

2. ....

....

> At present, the Sharma family live close to their family and friends. Yasir has recently accepted a new job, which means that the family will be moving to a new town 50 miles away.

(c) Identify **one** possible positive effect of Yasir's new job on his social development.   **(1 mark)**

....

....

(d) Identify **one** possible negative effect of Yasir's new job on his social development.   **(1 mark)**

....

....

Emotional and social development in infancy

1   The following information is about the staff and children at the Little Tots Nursery.
    Read the information and answer the questions below.

> Emma works in the infant room at the Little Tots Nursery, and cares for children aged from
> birth to 3 years. She knows that infancy is an important life stage for emotional and social
> development. Emma is the key worker for Logan, who is 5 months old, and Bella, who is
> 14 months.

Guided

(a) Identify **one** statement below that describes Logan's likely stage of emotional development
     and **one** statement that describes Bella's likely stage of emotional development.   **(2 marks)**

Draw lines to match Logan and Bella to their current stage of emotional development.

Names   **Stage of emotional development**

Logan   Is dependent on parents but is beginning to form bonds
                          with others

                          Becomes easily frustrated and often has temper tantrums

Bella   Has a strong attachment with parent or main carer

                          Has a strong bond with parent and is very wary of strangers

> Emma understands the importance of bonding and attachment.

(b) Outline the meaning of 'bonding and attachment'.   **(2 marks)**

....

....

> Leon is 2 years old. He is due to start at the nursery next week. Emma has arranged to meet
> with Leon's mum to talk about his stage of development so that she can help him to settle in.

(c) State **two** possible effects of starting nursery on Leon's social development.   **(2 marks)**

1. ....

....

2. ....

....

....

> Make sure that you state **two** different
> aspects of social development.
> Remember that developing
> independence is important for social
> development.

Emotional and social development in early childhood

1 The following information is about the Smith family.
Read the information and answer the questions below.

> Tyler, aged 6, and his sister Grace, aged 4, live with their mum. Tyler goes to the local school. Grace is due to start school next term.

Guided

(a) Give **two** characteristics of social development that Tyler is likely to be demonstrating at his life stage.
(2 marks)

1. He is forming relationships with adults other than his parents (teachers).

2. ....

(b) Assess the possible effects of starting school on Grace's emotional and social development
.
(8 marks)

....
....
....
....
....
....
....
....
....
....
....

> When assessing the possible effects on Grace's development, you must consider **all** the relevant factors relating to starting school. For instance, Grace will not spend as much time with her mum, she will be meeting new adults and children, and she will have a new routine that is unfamiliar. Link these changes in her life to her social and emotional development. For example, how will they affect how she feels about herself and others? How will they affect her feeling of security? Will they give her opportunities to make new friends and become independent?

....
....
....
....
....
....

> The best answer will balance the effects of both **emotional development** and **social development**.

Emotional and social development in adolescence

1 The following information is about Lauren and Theo.
Read the information and answer the questions below.

> Lauren is 12 years old. She lives with her parents and her older brother Theo, who is 16. Lauren is experiencing puberty, which is affecting her emotional development. She is unhappy because her skin is getting greasy and this is causing spots. Lauren finds it difficult to control her mood, which causes her to have arguments with her parents. She has developed a negative self-image.

 (a) (i) Give **two** possible reasons why Lauren has a negative self-image. **(2 marks)**

1. Lauren may not feel good about ....

2. Arguing with her parents may make Lauren feel ....

(ii) Identify **two** possible effects on Lauren's social development as a result of her negative self-image. **(2 marks)**

Put a cross in **two** boxes ☒ to indicate your answer.

A ☐ Lauren may be reluctant to go out and meet friends

B ☐ Lauren may have difficulty with her memory and recall

> Always read questions carefully. This question is asking you to think about the close **links** between emotional and social development.

C ☐ Lauren may do badly in end of term examinations

D ☐ Lauren may not want to take part in after-school activities

E ☐ Lauren may not complete homework on time

> Lauren's brother Theo has just achieved good grades for his exams at school and has been accepted by a local sixth form college to do a business course.

(b) Explain **one** possible effect of Theo's achievements on his emotional development. **(2 marks)**

....

....

(c) Explain **one** possible effect of Theo's achievements on his social development. **(2 marks)**

....

....

....

> Make sure that you explain an effect on **both** emotional **and** social development in your answers.

....

Emotional and social development in adulthood

1   The following information is about Madiha and Zoe.
Read the information and answer the questions below.

> Madiha, aged 42, has just moved in with her partner Zoe, who is 47. Zoe's daughter Gemma, aged 21, lives with them. Madiha works in a large department store and has just been promoted to manager.

(a) Give **two** possible effects of Madiha's promotion at work on her emotional development.

(2 marks)

1. ....

2. ....

> Zoe's daughter Gemma plans to leave home and work abroad next month.

Guided

(b) Explain **one** positive and **one** negative effect that Gemma's leaving home may have on Zoe's emotional and social development.   **(4 marks)**

Positive

Zoe may develop a closer relationship with Madiha, because they will have more time to

spend together when Gemma moves away.

Negative

Zoe may experience anxiety because ....

....

> Madiha's mum Saniya, aged 69, lives in a nearby town. Saniya has recently lost part of her sight, so she can no longer drive. This means that she is no longer able to visit her friends or Madiha as much as she used to.

(c) Give **two** possible effects of being unable to visit friends and family on Saniya's social development.   **(2 marks)**

1. ....

2. ....

Genetic inheritance

1   The following information is about Jamal.
    Read the information and answer the questions below.

> Jamal, aged 15, lives with his parents. He enjoys spending time with his dad, and enjoys the same hobbies. People often tell him that he looks like his dad.

Guided

   (a) Define the term 'genetic inheritance'.   **(2 marks)**

   Genetic inheritance is the passing of genes from parents to ....

   and how these genes ....

   ....

   ....

   (b) Which **two** of the following are examples of physical characteristics that Jamal may have
        inherited from his parents?   **(2 marks)**

   Put a cross in **two** boxes ☒ to indicate your answer.

   A   ☐   Eye colour

   B   ☐   Intelligence

   C   ☐   Height

   D   ☐   Musicality

   E   ☐   Confidence

2   The following information is about Ava.
    Read the information and answer the question below.

> Ava is 17 years old. She is studying A levels at college. Ava has a genetic disorder called cystic fibrosis, which causes her lungs and digestive system to become clogged with mucus. From time to time she has lung infections. Ava has to take medication for her disorder. She also has to have physiotherapy twice a day to help clear her lungs of mucus.

   Explain **two** possible effects that Ava's disorder may have on her growth and development.
                                                                               (4 marks)

   1. ....

   ....

   2. ....

   ....

17

Lifestyle choices

1   The following information is about the Ellis family.
Read the information and answer the questions below.

> Demaine and Paula live together. They have one child, Amy, who is 3. Demaine regularly drinks more than the recommended daily amount of alcohol. Paula understands the importance of a healthy diet, but the family often eats fast food.

> Guided

(a) Explain **two** possible effects of Demaine's drinking on his development.   **(4 marks)**

1. Drinking too much alcohol may affect Demaine's social development because it could

cause a breakdown in ....

2. Drinking too much alcohol may affect Demaine's intellectual development because it may

make it more difficult for Demaine ....

(b) Explain **two** possible effects of a healthy diet on the family's growth and development.

(4 marks)

1. ....

....

....

2. ....

....

....

(c) Explain **two** possible effects of an unhealthy diet on the family's growth and development.

(4 marks)

1. ....

....

....

2. ....

....

....

Illness and disease

1   The following information is about Nadia and her
mother Karolina.
Read the information and answer the questions below.

> Nadia lives alone. She works full time and has a
> busy social life. Her mother, Karolina, broke her hip
> recently. She is being cared for at home by the district
> nurse, but also needs support from Nadia.

Karolina uses a walking frame to help her to get around.

(a) Which type of development does a walking
frame support?   **(1 mark)**

Put a cross in **one** box ☒ to indicate your answer.

A   ☐   Intellectual development

B   ☐   Physical development

C   ☐   Social development

D   ☐   Emotional development

⯈ **Guided**   **(b)** Give **two** possible effects of Karolina's injury on her development.   **(2 marks)**

1. Loss of independence.

2. ....

(c) Explain **two** possible effects of Karolina's injury on Nadia's development.   **(4 marks)**

1. ....

....

2. ....

....

> Read the question carefully. This
> question requires you to think about
> the effect on **Nadia** rather than her
> mother, Karolina. Remember that
> illness and injury can affect others in
> a family, not just the person who is ill
> or injured.

The influence of play

1   The following information is about Madge.
Read the information and answer the questions below.

> Madge is a child-minder. She cares for three children:
> Amir aged 7, Humayra aged 4, and Timmy, who is
> 12 months. Timmy enjoys puppet play.

(a) Which aspect of language development is puppet play
most important for?   **(1 mark)**

Put a cross in **one** box ☒ to indicate your answer.

A ☐   Memory and recall   B ☐   Speech and vocabulary

C ☐   Problem solving   D ☐   Creative thinking

> Timmy enjoys solitary play. Amir and Humayra like to take part in social play.

⟩ **Guided** ⟩   **(b)** Outline the difference between 'solitary play' and 'social play'.   **(2 marks)**

In solitary play, children play alone or alongside others, but in social play, they ....

....

> Madge wants to provide activities that will promote each child's emotional development.

(c) For **each** child, give an example of an activity that could be used to promote their emotional
development.   **(3 marks)**

Complete the table below.

Child	Activity
Amir	
Humayra	
Timmy	

Culture

1 The following information is about Ellen.
   Read the information and answer the question below.

> Ellen is 74 and lives alone. Ellen is a Christian and a member of her local church.

Give **two** examples of positive effects of Ellen's religious beliefs on her emotional and social development.   **(2 marks)**

1. ....

2. ....

Guided **2** The following information is about the Danchev family.
   Read the information and answer the question below.

> Georgi and his wife Tanja have recently moved to the UK from Bulgaria. They live in a flat in an area where there is a small community of families from their home country. They both have full-time jobs, but sometimes experience negative comments at work about their background.

Assess the possible impact of culture on Georgi and Tanja's development.   **(8 marks)**

Having people from their home country living close by will help Georgi and Tanja to ....

.... Having people from their home country

living close by may also mean that they feel happier and more confident, as they share

.... They are

likely to feel more secure and contented with people who speak the ....

.... and who have the same ....

.... They have both secured jobs in the UK, which is likely

to boost their .... because others have recognised their abilities.

Georgi and Tanja could face discrimination because ....

....

....

This may cause them to feel ....

....

....

Lack of acceptance because of their culture may put a strain on ....

....

....

If other people do not understand Georgi and Tanja's culture and values, the couple may find

it difficult to develop a wider ....

Gender

1 Define the term 'gender inequality'.   **(1 mark)**

....

....

....

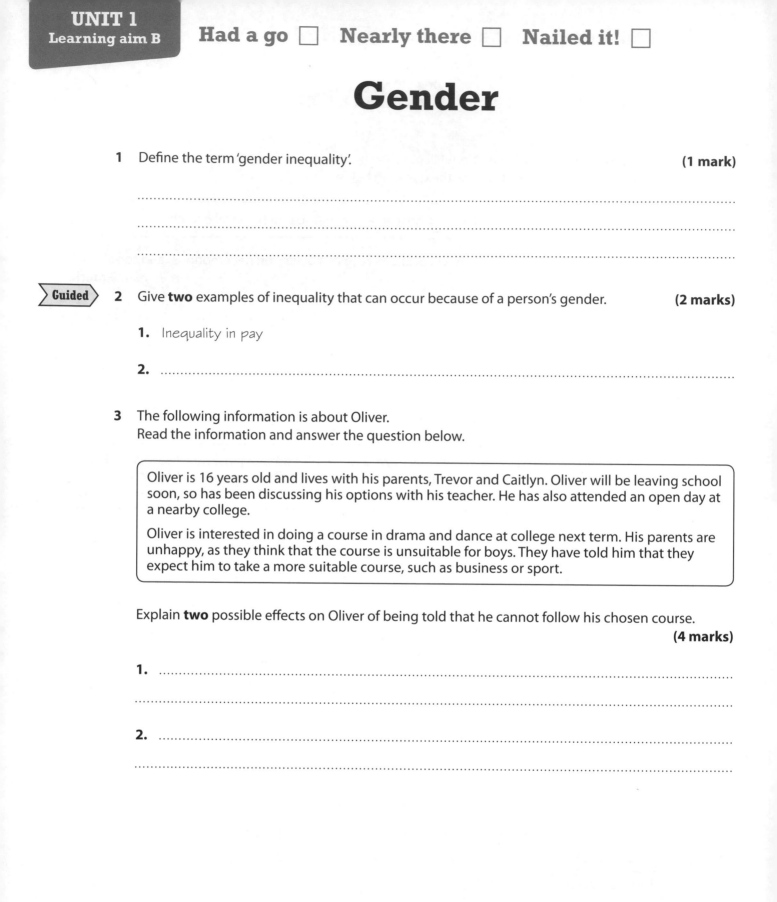

Guided **2** Give **two** examples of inequality that can occur because of a person's gender.   **(2 marks)**

1. Inequality in pay

2. ....

3 The following information is about Oliver.
Read the information and answer the question below.

Oliver is 16 years old and lives with his parents, Trevor and Caitlyn. Oliver will be leaving school soon, so has been discussing his options with his teacher. He has also attended an open day at a nearby college.

Oliver is interested in doing a course in drama and dance at college next term. His parents are unhappy, as they think that the course is unsuitable for boys. They have told him that they expect him to take a more suitable course, such as business or sport.

Explain **two** possible effects on Oliver of being told that he cannot follow his chosen course.

(4 marks)

1. ....

....

2. ....

....

Role models and social isolation

⟩ **Guided** ⟩ **1** The following information is about Abbie and Hayley.
Read the information and answer the question below.

> Abbie, who is 5 years old, has started school. Hayley, the teaching assistant, understands that it is important to be a good role model for Abbie.

Give **two** examples of how Hayley can be a positive role model for Abbie.　　　**(2 marks)**

1. Hayley can demonstrate how to share and ....

....

2. Hayley can show respect when ....

....

2 The following information is about Vera.
Read the information and answer the questions below.

> Vera, who is 76 years old, lives alone as her husband Jeff died last year. She used to visit friends and go to a day centre each week, but since Jeff died, she has been reluctant to go out and socialise. Vera is experiencing social isolation.

(a) Define the term 'social isolation'.　　　**(1 mark)**

....

....

(b) Explain **two** ways in which social isolation may affect Vera's development.　　　**(4 marks)**

1. ....

....

2. ....

....

Economic factors

1   The following information is about Seema.
Read the information and answer the questions below.

> Seema is 42, and is married to Scott. They both work full time. Last year they bought a new house. They could just about manage to pay for the mortgage on their joint income. Last month, Seema was made redundant from her job as an accounts manager.

Guided

(a) Describe **two** possible effects of redundancy on Seema's relationship with Scott.   **(4 marks)**

1.   Seema may feel guilty about not being able to contribute to the household bills, which

may put pressure on their relationship.

2.   ....

....

> Seema has been offered a part-time job cleaning offices. She is happy to have a job, but the salary is much less money than she earned before.

(b) Explain **one** positive effect of being offered this job on Seema's development.   **(2 marks)**

....

....

(c) Explain **one** negative effect of being offered this job on Seema's development.   **(2 marks)**

....

....

Physical environment

Guided 1 The following information is about Valerie and Ken.
Read the information and answer the question below.

> Valerie, aged 54, and her husband Ken, 53, live in a small village. A quarry has just opened close by, which means that heavy lorries constantly pass their house. Valerie and Ken are concerned about the pollution that the lorries cause.

Give **two** possible effects of pollution on Valerie and Ken's health.   **(2 marks)**

1. Cancers

2. ....

2 The following information is about Kath and her family.
Read the information and answer the questions below.

> Kath is 22 years old and lives with her partner Dean, who is 24. They have two children, John, aged 5 and Kyle, who is 12 months. The family live with Kath's parents in a small two-bedroom flat.

(a) Identify **two** possible effects of overcrowding on Kath's growth and development.   **(2 marks)**

1. ....

....

2. ....

....

> Kath and Dean have been offered a new house by their local authority. The house has three bedrooms and a garden.

(b) Explain **two** possible effects of moving to the new house on John and Kyle's growth and development.   **(4 marks)**

1. ....

....

....

2. ....

....

....

Family relationships

1 The following information is about Nasim and Omar.
Read the information and answer the questions below.

> Nasim lives with his parents and his brother Omar. He has a close relationship with both his parents and his brother. The whole family is proud of him, as he has just completed his A levels and has a place at university. Nasim is well liked and has lots of friends. He has a positive self-image.

(a) Give **two** possible reasons why Nasim has a positive self-image.   **(2 marks)**

1. ....

2. ....

> Guided

(b) Explain **two** possible effects of Nasim's close relationship with his family on his development.
(4 marks)

1. The love and support from his family will enable Nasim to ....

....

2. As Nasim has a good relationship with his family, he is more likely to be able to build and

develop ....

> Nasim's brother Omar has recently been in trouble with the police for theft. His parents have asked Omar to leave the house, and will not speak to him.

(c) Explain **two** effects of the breakdown in family relationships on Omar's development.
(4 marks)

1. ....

....

2. ....

....

Friendships and relationships

1 The following information is about Graham and Sally.
   Read the information and answer the questions below.

> Graham, aged 40, is married to Sally, who is 42. They have one son, Alfie, who has just turned 16. Sally has multiple sclerosis and needs a lot of support at home. She has help from a carer while Graham is at work all day, but he then spends his evenings and weekends caring for Sally.

> Guided

(a) Explain **two** possible effects of Sally's illness on Graham's emotional and social development.

(4 marks)

1. As most of his time is spent caring for Sally, Graham may not have any time to ....
....
....

> When a question asks you to explain the effects on different aspects of development, make sure that you include an example for each type of development given in the question.

2. The relationship between Graham and Sally may break down as ....
....
....

> Alfie is Graham's son from a previous relationship. Recently, Alfie has started dating a girl he met at school.

(b) Give **two** possible effects of Alfie's new relationship on his emotional development.

(2 marks)

1. ....

2. ....

Stress

1 The following information is about Kesh.
   Read the information and answer the questions below.

> Kesh is 29. He lives with his partner Leo, who is 28. They have two children. Kesh works as a car salesman. His job is not going well, as his boss has given him very high sales targets to meet this month. Kesh's dad has recently had a heart attack, so Kesh has been visiting him in hospital each day.

Guided

(a) Give **two** reasons why Kesh may feel stressed.   (2 marks)

1. Kesh will be worried about his dad's health.

2. ....

(b) Explain **two** possible effects of stress on Kesh's emotional development.   (4 marks)

1. ....

   ....

   ....

2. ....

   ....

   ....

   ....

   ....

> This question asks you to explain the effects of stress on emotional development **only**. If you jot down the different aspects of emotional development that could be affected by stress – for example, security, self-image, self-esteem and contentment – this will help you to think about how each one might be affected in Kesh's situation.

Expected life events 1

1   The following information is about the Williams family.
Read the information and answer the questions below.

> Adam is 44 years old and is happily married to Stella, who is 38. They have twins, Megan and
> Jasper, who are 8 years old.

(a) Identify **two** expected life events that Megan and Jasper are likely to have experienced at
their life stage.

(2 marks)

1. ....

2. ....

> Guided

(b) Identify **two** possible expected life events that the twins may experience later in their lives.

(2 marks)

1. Leaving school

2. ....

(c) Identify **two** expected life events that Adam and Stella are likely to have experienced at their
life stage.

(2 marks)

1. ....

2. ....

29

Expected life events 2

1   The following information is about Phil and Sacha.
Read the information and answer the questions below.

> Phil, aged 33, and Sacha, aged 30, got married last year. They are expecting their first baby in two months.

(a) Give **one** possible positive effect and **one** possible negative effect of getting married on Phil's development.   **(2 marks)**

Positive

....

Negative

....

Guided

(b) Explain **two** possible effects of having a baby on Sacha's development.   **(4 marks)**

1. Sacha may develop a sense of contentment and wellbeing because ....

....

....

2. She may lose her independence because ....

....

....

Unexpected life events 1

1 The following information is about Sylvia and Malcolm.
   Read the information and answer the questions below.

> Sylvia is 64 and Malcolm is 68. They married 40 years ago. Until recently, Sylvia worked part time in a shop. She was made redundant. Malcolm retired three years ago. Last month, he fell and broke his hip. Sylvia and Malcolm had one son, Matthew, but two years ago he was killed in a motorcycle accident.

Guided

(a) Outline the difference between 'expected life events' and 'unexpected life events'. **(2 marks)**

.... life events are events that may happen to most people

during the course of their life.

.... life events are events that only happen to some people.

They can't be predicted.

(b) Identify **two** unexpected life events that Sylvia has experienced. **(2 marks)**

1. ....

2. ....

> Make sure that you only give **unexpected** life events in your answers. Sylvia and Malcolm have experienced a number of events in their life; many will have been expected. Events may have affected both Sylvia and Malcolm.

(c) Identify **two** unexpected life events that Malcolm has experienced. **(2 marks)**

1. ....

2. ....

Unexpected life events 2

1   The following information is about Sean.
Read the information and answer the questions below.

> Sean is 15 years old and attends a local secondary school. He was in a fight at school last week, and another boy got badly hurt. Sean's mum was called to the school to meet with the head teacher to discuss his behaviour. Sean has now been excluded for the rest of the term.

(a) Give **two** possible ways in which Sean's exclusion from school may affect his mum.   **(2 marks)**

1. ....

2. ....

(b) Assess the possible effects on Sean's growth and development of being excluded from school.
    (8 marks)

....
....
....
....
....
....
....
....
....
....
....
....
....
....
....
....
....
....
....

> When answering this question, consider all the factors relating to this event in Sean's life, and then explore how these may affect each aspect of his development.
> - For instance, what could be the effects on his developing friendships and how might this affect his social development?
> - What about the effects on his independence and confidence, and how might that affect his development?
> - How will missing classes impact on Sean's learning?
> - How will the behaviour of others towards him affect how Sean sees himself?
> - Could missing school activities have any effects on his physical development?

Types of support

1 The following information is about Helen.
   Read the information and answer the question below.

> Helen is 65 years old and suffers from arthritis. She
> attends regular physiotherapy sessions.

Which **two** types of support is the physiotherapist
giving?   **(2 marks)**

Put a cross in **two** boxes ☒ to indicate your answer.

A ☐ Formal   B ☐ Emotional   C ☐ Informal

D ☐ Physical   E ☐ Intellectual

2 The following information is about Qas and Lisa.
   Read the information and answer the questions below.

> Qas is 45 and his partner Lisa is 37. They have one child, Tia, who is 3 months old. Qas recently
> had a heart attack and has had to give up work.

Guided

(a) For each type of support, give a specific example of the kind of support that may be given to
    Qas following his heart attack.   **(2 marks)**

Complete the table below.

Type of support	Support given
Formal	Physical check-up
Informal	

> Lisa is finding it hard to cope. She is getting stressed as a result of having to deal with Qas's
> health concerns, and also because she feels that she isn't looking after Tia very well.

(b) Explain **two** examples of emotional support that could help Lisa manage the changes in her
    life.   **(4 marks)**

1. ....

....

....

2. ....

....

....

Managing change 1

1   The following information is about Nadine.
    Read the information and answer the questions below.

> Nadine, aged 54, lives with her husband Glen, who is 55. Last month Nadine had a stroke. As a result, the right side of her body is very weak. She has great difficulty walking and using her right arm. She has been discharged from hospital, but she still feels very ill and she is worried that she may not regain her strength. Nadine is visited regularly by the district nurse.

(a) Identify **two** specific types of support that the district nurse might give Nadine.   **(2 marks)**

1.   ....

2.   ....

Guided

(b) Identify **two** specific types of support that Nadine's husband, Glen, might give Nadine.

(2 marks)

1.   Help with coming to terms with changes in her health

2.   ....

> Nadine's good friend Anna visits her regularly to have a chat. She sometimes takes Nadine out to meet other friends.

(c) Explain **two** ways in which Anna's support may help Nadine to manage the changes in her life.
(4 marks)

1.   ....

....

....

2.   ....

....

....

Managing change 2

1 The following information is about Rehana.
   Read the information and answer the question below.

> Rehana, 64, is a Muslim. She lives with her son and her daughter-in-law. Rehana has recently been diagnosed with diabetes. She is being supported by her GP and a district nurse. Because she is so worried about her diagnosis, her son has suggested that she contacts her local Muslim organisation for help.

Outline the role of religious organisations in helping individuals to manage change caused by life events. **(2 marks)**

....

....

....

Guided 2 The following information is about Sonia and Russell.
   Read the information and answer the question below.

> Sonia is 34 years old and lives with her partner Russell, who is 31. Sonia has just been diagnosed with breast cancer. She is receiving formal support from her doctor and the district nurse. Her friend has suggested that she contacts a voluntary cancer organisation to help her to manage the change she is experiencing.

Explain **two** ways in which a voluntary organisation could support Sonia to manage her illness. **(4 marks)**

1. A voluntary cancer organisation may help Sonia to make decisions about her illness because they will be able to give her specific information about ....

....

2. Volunteers who work for the organisation are more likely to be able to help Sonia come to terms with her illness because ....

....

Had a go ☐   Nearly there ☐   Nailed it! ☐

Exam skills 1

1 The following information is about Medina and her family.
Read the information and answer the questions below.

> Max is 42 years old and is happily married to Medina, 36. They have three children. Ami is 14, Carrie 8 and Stuart 20 months. Max works full time as a nurse. Ami and Carrie go to school. Stuart goes to a nursery each morning.

(a) Draw lines to match Medina and Carrie to their current life stage.   **(2 marks)**

Names

Medina

Carrie

Life stage

Infancy

Early childhood

Adolescence

Early adulthood

Middle adulthood

> Medina has just started a new job at the local supermarket.

Guided

(b) Explain **two** possible effects of starting work on Medina's development.   **(4 marks)**

1. Medina may develop a positive self-image because ....
....
....

2. ....
....
....
....
....

> This question asks you to **explain**. This means that you not only need to state that Medina's self-image may be improved by starting her new job but that you also need to give a reason why it has been as well.

Exam skills 2

1 The following information is about Conrad and Emily.
Read the information and answer the questions below.

> Conrad, 69, is married to Emily, 67. They are both retired. They have lots of friends. They enjoy gardening and going to the cinema. At their life stage Conrad and Emily are experiencing the ageing process.

Guided

(a) Define the term 'ageing process'.   **(1 mark)**

The ageing process describes the physical changes that take place in ....

....

(b) Give **two** examples of the ageing process on Conrad's physical development.   **(2 marks)**

1. ....

2. ....

> Emily has recently had heart problems.

(c) Give **two** specific types of support that the district nurse might provide to help Emily.
     (2 marks)

1. ....

2. ....

Exam skills 3

1   The following information is about the Fahmi family.
Read the information and answer the questions below.

> Rafael, 54, lives with Malika, 50. They have two children, Ola, 19 and Aleksandra, 16. Rafael and Malika work full time. They both have good jobs that pay well. Rafael works as a chef. Malika works as a deputy head teacher in a secondary school.

Guided

(a) Explain **two** possible effects of Malika's occupation on her emotional development.   **(4 marks)**

1.   Malika will feel secure because she has security of income ....

....

....

2.   ....

....

....

....

> There could be a number of effects on Malika's development. Make sure you only consider the effects on her **emotional** development.

> Ola recently dropped out of college because she was not coping with the work.

(b) Explain **two** possible effects of dropping out of college on Ola's growth and development.

(4 marks)

1.   ....

....

2.   ....

....

....

....

> In the first question you needed to focus on aspects of emotional development only, but here you should consider the effects on **any** of the areas of development. Try to include at least two areas.

Exam skills 4

 1   The following information is about the Colbert family.
Read the information and answer the question below.

> Jermaine, 42 was married to Arlene for 15 years. They have a son Dillon, who is 13. Last year, Jermaine's and Arlene's marriage broke down. Arlene left the family home and Dillon now lives with his dad. Arlene now lives in a different town, which means that Dillon can only visit at weekends.

Assess the possible effects of the family breakdown on Dillon's development.   **(8 marks)**

Because Dillon's mother left the family home, the close bonds he had with her may break

down because he does not see her every day. Dillon may feel less secure and contented,

which may ....

....

....

....

....

....

....

....

....

....

....

....

....

....

....

....

....

....

....

....

....

> Jot down some ideas before you start and check that you have thought about different aspects of development. Many of your ideas may be about the negative effects caused by the family breakdown. Can you think of any positive effects?

Defining health and wellbeing

1 Health and wellbeing are influenced by a range of biological and lifestyle factors.

Which **one** of the following is the World Health Organization's (WHO) definition of health and wellbeing? **(1 mark)**

Put a cross in **one** box ☒ to indicate your answer.

A ☐ The absence of physical illness, disease and mental distress

B ☐ The achievement and maintenance of physical fitness and mental stability, and not merely the absence of disease

C ☐ A complete state of physical fitness

D ☐ A complete state of physical, mental and social wellbeing, and not merely the absence of disease or infirmity

(Source: WHO, 1948)

2 Luisa is 24 years old and works as a teacher. She lives near her parents and sees them regularly. She enjoys exercise, tries to go for a run three times a week and attends a weekly 'boxercise' class. She meets up with her friends most weekends.

> **Guided**

(a) Identify **two** ways in which Luisa's needs are currently being met. **(2 marks)**

> Make sure you think about PIES when answering this question.

1. Luisa's physical needs are being met by boxercise and running.

2. ....

(b) Explain whether Luisa's health and wellbeing are holistic. **(2 marks)**

....

....

3 Joe is homeless and lives on the streets. He sometimes visits a refuge for a hot meal, a drink and some company.

Explain which **two** of Joe's needs are being partially met by the refuge. **(4 marks)**

1. ....

....

2. ....

....

Physical and intellectual factors

> **Guided**

1 A balanced diet is important in maintaining a healthy lifestyle.

Explain **two** ways in which eating a balanced diet can have a positive effect on physical and intellectual wellbeing. **(4 marks)**

> Pick an example of a healthy lifestyle choice and use it to give one effect on physical wellbeing and one effect on intellectual wellbeing.

1. Eating a balanced diet can lead to weight loss, making it easier to ....

....

2. Eating a balanced diet provides the minerals and other ....

....

....

2 Anya is 16 years old and is an only child. Her parents are Russian and they speak Russian at home, so Anya is bilingual, and she likes to read books in both languages. They live in a two-bedroom terraced house, so Anya has her own bedroom. The house is in the centre of a busy town, with a very small yard at the back. The house is small but well cared for by her parents. Anya works hard at school.

> 'Bilingual' means that Anya speaks two languages fluently.

(a) Explain **two** ways in which Anya's home environment may affect her physical wellbeing. **(4 marks)**

1. ....

....

2. ....

....

(b) Explain **two** ways in which Anya's home environment may affect her intellectual wellbeing. **(4 marks)**

1. ....

....

2. ....

....

Emotional and social effects

1 Drinking too much alcohol is a risk to health and wellbeing.

Explain **two** ways in which drinking too much alcohol can have a negative effect on emotional and social wellbeing. **(4 marks)**

1. ....
....
....
....

> Make sure you give one effect on emotional wellbeing and one effect on social wellbeing.

....

2. ....
....

2 Will is 75 years old and suffers from arthritis. As a result, he is always in pain, has mobility problems and finds it hard to do much for himself. He has help from carers, who visit him first thing in the morning and last thing at night. Various family members also visit him most days.

Guided

(a) Explain **two** ways in which Will's arthritis is negatively affecting his emotional and social wellbeing. **(4 marks)**

1. Will's arthritis means he is in pain most of the time, which could negatively affect his mood if he cannot concentrate on anything else.

2. Will's pain and .... problems mean that he doesn't get out much. Therefore, ...
....

(b) Identify **two** ways in which Will's carers and family have a positive effect on his emotional and social wellbeing and his lifestyle. **(2 marks)**

1. ....
....

2. ....
....

Physical effects of an unhealthy lifestyle

1 Jada is 20 years old. She has recently moved away from home and is living in poor conditions. Jada has started taking recreational drugs with a group of friends. She doesn't have much money and spends what she has on drugs.

> **Guided**

   (a) State **two** possible risks of Jada's unhealthy lifestyle for her health.   **(2 marks)**

   1. She will have an increased risk of illness/disease due to ....

   ....

   2. She may have a poor diet, resulting in ....

   ....

   (b) State **two** ways in which Jada's lifestyle choice is having a negative effect on her physical wellbeing.   **(2 marks)**

   > In part **(b)**, avoid answers that repeat what you have written in your answer to part **(a)**.

   1. ....

   ....

   ....

   2. ....

   ....

2 Tom is 69 years old. He met Sian at a salsa dancing class about six months ago. They now live together. Sian drinks at least three glasses of wine every day and Tom has started to do the same.

   Explain **two** ways in which Tom's change of lifestyle may affect his physical wellbeing.   **(4 marks)**

   1. ....

   ....

   2. ....

   ....

Intellectual effects of an unhealthy lifestyle

Guided 1 An unhealthy lifestyle is a risk to health and wellbeing.

Which **two** of the following are examples of intellectual effects of an unhealthy lifestyle?

(2 marks)

Put a cross in **two** boxes ☒ to indicate your answer.

A ☒ Reduced success in education

B ☐ Weight gain/loss

C ☐ Poor long-term career prospects

D ☐ Low self-esteem

E ☐ Higher likelihood of heart disease

> Remember to think carefully about what type of need an **intellectual need is** before answering the questions on this page. Do not confuse intellectual needs with physical, emotional or social needs.

2 Zaid is 80 years old. He lives by himself and rarely leaves the house. His only son lives abroad. Zaid's eyesight has started to decline, so he no longer reads as much and he has no one to take him to get new glasses.

(a) Identify **two** ways in which Zaid is likely to be affected intellectually by his lifestyle. **(2 marks)**

1. ....

....

2. ....

....

(b) State **two** ways in which Zaid's intellectual needs could be met if his son moved back to Britain and invited his father to live with him. **(2 marks)**

1. ....

....

2. ....

....

Emotional effects of an unhealthy lifestyle

1   Tanvi is 26 years old. She lives in a two-bedroom flat with her husband Nikhil, her 6-month-old daughter Riya and her grandmother, Priya, who is 76 years old. Tanvi stays at home with Riya and Priya while Nikhil goes to work. She is suffering from postnatal depression.

Guided

(a) Explain **two** ways in which Tanvi's lifestyle is negatively affecting her emotional wellbeing.

(4 marks)

1. Tanvi is finding it hard to cope emotionally because she is suffering from postnatal depression. This makes her feel like she is letting Riya down which makes her upset.

2. ....

....

Tanvi relies heavily on her friend Kim for support.

(b) Describe **two** ways in which Kim may affect Tanvi's emotional wellbeing in a positive way.

(4 marks)

1. ....

....

2. ....

....

2   Sophie is 18 years old. She is quiet, shy and overweight. In September she will be going to university, but she is anxious about meeting and living with new people. Sophie wants to join some clubs or societies, but is worried about joining ones that do physical activities.

Identify **two** ways in which Sophie's weight is affecting her emotional health and wellbeing.

(2 marks)

1. ....

....

....

| Remember that emotional needs are those to do with feelings. |

2. ....

....

Social effects of an unhealthy lifestyle

> **Guided**

1 Oscar is 88 years old and lives in a residential care home. His son and daughter visit once a week. The carers have little spare time to help Oscar walk to the dining room, so he often eats in his room.

Identify **two** ways in which living in the care home is having a negative social effect on Oscar's wellbeing. **(2 marks)**

1. Oscar often eats alone in his room, so ....

....

2. He only sees his family once a week, so ....

....

....

> Social needs are those to do with getting on with others.

2 Susan is 60 years old and lives on her own. She looks after her grandchildren every day until their parents come home. She used to smoke 40 cigarettes a day but is cutting down, because she doesn't want to look bad by smoking at the school gate.

(a) Name **two** ways in which looking after her grandchildren is having a positive effect on Susan's social wellbeing and helping her achieve a healthier lifestyle. **(2 marks)**

1. ....

....

2. ....

....

Susan's husband died two years ago and she misses him very much.

(b) Identify **two** ways in which her husband's death may have affected Susan's social wellbeing.
(2 marks)

1. ....

....

2. ....

....

Diet and nutrition

1 A balanced diet is an important part of maintaining a healthy lifestyle.

(a) Which **two** of the following are examples of nutrients?   **(2 marks)**

Put a cross in **two** boxes ☒ to indicate your answer.

A ☐ Water

B ☐ Carbohydrate

C ☐ Carbon dioxide

D ☐ Fibre

E ☐ Protein

> If you change your mind, put a line though the box and put a cross in the box you have chosen as your right answer.

(b) State **two** long-term health risks of excessive weight loss due to under-eating.   **(2 marks)**

1. ....

2. ....

2 Jenna is 15 years old. She is very overweight but often misses breakfast. As her parents work long hours, they often eat fast food, such as fish and chips, in the evening.

> **Guided**

(a) Give **two** physical effects of Jenna's unbalanced diet.   **(2 marks)**

1. Weight gain

2. ....

(b) Explain **two** ways in which Jenna could improve her diet.   **(4 marks)**

1. ....

....

2. ....

....

Exercise

1   Sam is 1.83 m tall and weighs 114 kg.

 (a) Calculate Sam's Body Mass Index (BMI).   **(2 marks)**

$$BMI = \frac{(Weight\ in\ kg)}{(Height\ in\ m)^2}$$

$$BMI = \frac{(114)}{(1.83 \times 1.83)}$$

> Show your working and calculate the BMI to one decimal place.

BMI = ... kg/m²

(b) Using Table A, select Sam's BMI rating.   **(1 mark)**

Put a cross in **one** box ☒ to indicate your answer.

BMI	Rating
<19	Underweight
20–25	Desirable
26–30	Overweight
31+	Obese

Table A

A ☐ Underweight

B ☐ Desirable

C ☐ Overweight

D ☐ Obese

(c) Identify **two** benefits to Sam of taking part in exercise regularly.   **(2 marks)**

1. ....

2. ....

Home environment

1 A good home environment is important to health and wellbeing.

Which **two** of the following are possible physical effects of living in a poor home environment?

(2 marks)

Put a cross in **two** boxes ☒ to indicate your answer.

A ☐ Increased risk of becoming ill

B ☐ More chance of making a health problem worse

C ☐ Increased risk of relationships breaking down

D ☐ Less chance of being able to concentrate

E ☐ Withdrawing from friendships as do not want to invite them home

2 Chan is 13 years old and lives with her mother and three younger sisters. Her mother works long hours and has little time for housework. Chan shares a bedroom with her sister, who likes to play her music loudly. Chan does not like to invite her friends over, because she is too embarrassed by the untidiness and the noise.

Guided

(a) Explain **two** ways in which Chan's home environment may be affecting her health and wellbeing in a negative way. **(4 marks)**

> When a question asks about health and wellbeing, think about PIES. This will ensure that your answer covers each of the four types of need.

1. Chan is unable to get any peace to do her homework, which may ....

....

2. Chan is too embarrassed to invite her friends round. They may think she is being unfriendly and stop ....

Even though the house is untidy, Chan's mother always keeps it clean. Her sisters are often at home.

(b) Identify **two** positive effects of Chan's home environment on her health and wellbeing.

(2 marks)

1. ....

....

2. ....

....

Work environment

1   A good work/life balance is an important part of a healthy lifestyle.

Give **two** effects of a poor work/life balance.   **(2 marks)**

1. ....

   ....

2. ....

   ....

> If you use PIES to identify two completely different types of negative effect (for example, physical and emotional), you are unlikely to give the same answer twice.

2   Jim is 52 years old and has worked in the same factory for 18 years. He gets on well with his colleagues and sees some of them socially. He does a skilled job and his line manager often praises his work. The factory is noisy. Jim has developed a painful wrist condition from using the same tools all day.

Guided

(a) Give **two** ways in which Jim's work environment is affecting his health and wellbeing negatively.

(2 marks)

> Imagine yourself in Jim's work environment and how it might affect you.

1. His work environment is very noisy, which may cause ....

   ....

2. As he works with his hands using the same tools all day, he has already ....

   ....

(b) Explain **two** positive effects of Jim's work environment on his health and wellbeing.

(4 marks)

1. ....

   ....

2. ....

   ....

Alcohol consumption

1 Drinking too much alcohol can have a negative effect on health and wellbeing. Moderate amounts of alcohol can be beneficial.

What is the recommended maximum number of units of alcohol per week for men and women?

(1 mark)

Put a cross in **one** box ☒ to indicate your answer.

A ☐ Men: 70 units / Women: 35 units

B ☐ Men: 21 units / Women: 14 units

C ☐ Men: 10 units / Women: 7 units

D ☐ Men: 14 units / Women: 21 units

2 Hannah is 16 years old and binge drinks with her friends every weekend.

(a) Define 'binge drinking'. **(1 mark)**

....

> **Guided**

(b) Explain **two** ways in which binge drinking may affect Hannah's health and wellbeing.

(4 marks)

> Think about a short-term effect and a long-term effect. That way, you will pick two different answers.

1. Hannah's judgement may be impaired, so ....

....

2. ....

....

3 Ash used to drink excessively with his friends. He has recently stopped drinking.

Give **two** physical effects of stopping drinking on Ash. **(2 marks)**

1. ....

2. ....

Effects of alcohol

1 Keane is 22 years old and drinks with his friends. Every week he drinks more than the recommended daily number of units.

> **Guided**

(a) Give **two** possible short-term effects of drinking too much on Keane's health and wellbeing.

(2 marks)

> Remember that a short-term effect refers to either an immediate effect or one that happens within a few weeks.

1. Keane might injure himself due to impaired judgement.

2. ....

....

(b) Give **two** possible long-term effects of drinking too much on Keane's health and wellbeing.

(2 marks)

1. ....

....

2. ....

....

2 Carol wants to cut down on her drinking. She often goes for several drinks with her friends after work. At the weekend, she usually goes out to a bar with her boyfriend.

Suggest **two** ways in which her boyfriend and friends could help Carol reduce her alcohol intake.

(2 marks)

1. ....

....

2. ....

....

Smoking

1   Smoking causes risks to health and wellbeing.

Which **two** of the following are health risks associated with smoking?   **(2 marks)**

Put a cross in **two** boxes ☒ to indicate your answer.

A ☐   Lung cancer

B ☐   Insomnia

C ☐   Rapid mood swings

D ☐   Bronchitis

E ☐   Depression

2   Alka is 15 years old and smokes about 20 cigarettes a day. He started when he was 13 because the group of friends he used to hang around with smoked.

Guided

   (a) Give **two** short-term physical effects of smoking.   **(2 marks)**

    1.   Increased blood pressure

    2. ....

Alka has recently started a new school and has a new group of friends who don't like him smoking.

> Think what you could do to help if one of your friends smoked in a group of non-smokers.

   (b) Explain **two** ways in which peer pressure could help Alka stop smoking.   **(4 marks)**

    1. ....

    ....

    2. ....

    ....

Recreational drug use

1   Read the information about Barbara in the box below.

> Barbara is 40 years old. She has no children and she was quite happy spending her leisure time with her husband and the friends that they had made through his work. A year ago, Barbara's marriage broke down.
>
> At about the same time, she met an old school friend at a school reunion who introduced her to some new people. Her new friends are single or divorced women who meet up every weekend. They enjoy going to clubs and taking recreational drugs. Some of them smoke and they all enjoy quite a few alcoholic drinks. Barbara quickly became part of the group.
>
> Barbara is not addicted to drugs, but enjoys taking them. She also smokes and drinks more alcohol than she used to.
>
> She is close to her family. Her parents and sister are all worried about the changes in her life. They have asked her to stop taking recreational drugs. They don't like her smoking and drinking, but it is the recreational drugs they are most worried about.

Guided

(a) Describe **one** way in which Barbara's recreational drug use could lead to illness and disease.

(2 marks)

> Read the case study at least twice and highlight sections that you think are important.

She will be more likely to get ill as her ....

.... will be weakened by drug use.

(b) Evaluate the likelihood of Barbara achieving her family's wish of giving up recreational drugs.

(8 marks)

....

....

....

....

> Make sure you think of some positive and some negative reasons for giving up drugs, to give a balanced argument.

....

....

....

....

....

....

....

....

> At the end, write a conclusion based on the points you have made.

....

....

Sexual practices

1   Safe sex is essential to good health and wellbeing.

   Which **two** of the following are safe sexual practices?   **(2 marks)**

   Put a cross in **two** boxes ☒ to indicate your answer.

   A ☐ Lots of sexual partners

   B ☐ Using barrier methods of contraception

   C ☐ Taking part in sexual health screening

   D ☐ Using a condom only until you get to know your new sexual partner

   E ☐ Drinking excessive amounts of alcohol before engaging in sexual activity

2   Sevanna is 16 years old and sometimes has unsafe sex.

   (a) State **two** physical risks of unsafe sexual practices.   **(2 marks)**

   > Read the question carefully to make sure you give the correct type of risk – in this case, physical.

   1. ....

   ....

   2. ....

   Guided

   (b) Identify **two** groups of people or places Sevanna could go to for advice if she has had unsafe sex and is concerned.   **(2 marks)**

   1. Sevanna could go to speak to her doctor.

   2. ....

   ....

   (c) State **two** ways that safe sex will improve Sevanna's emotional wellbeing.   **(2 marks)**

   1. ....

   ....

   2. ....

   ....

Personal hygiene

1   Good personal hygiene is important in maintaining a healthy lifestyle.

(a) Which of the following is an example of poor personal hygiene?   **(1 mark)**

Put a cross in **one** box ☒ to indicate your answer.

A ☐ Eating a healthy diet

B ☐ Changing your clothes once a week

C ☐ Cleaning your teeth twice a day

D ☐ Drinking two litres of water a day

> **Guided**

(b) Explain **two** reasons why good personal hygiene is
an important part of a healthy lifestyle.

(4 marks)

> 'Explain' means that you not only
> have to state a reason, but also
> explain that reason.

1.   You are less likely to have harmful bacteria or germs on your skin or in other

parts of your body, such as your mouth, which means you will be less likely to

....

2.   You will smell fresh, so others will be happy to be around you and be your friend, which

will mean ....

....

2   Johnny is 45 years old. He only showers once a week. He has to wear a suit to work and sweats
a lot.

Explain how Johnny's poor personal hygiene may affect him socially and emotionally.   **(4 marks)**

....

....

....

....

....

....

Sleep patterns

1 A regular sleep pattern is essential in leading a healthy lifestyle.

(a) Give **two** benefits of a regular sleep pattern.   **(2 marks)**

1. ....

2. ....

(b) State **one** way in which a person's work environment can have a negative effect on their sleep
pattern.   **(1 mark)**

....

Guided   **2** Read the information about Natalia in the box below.

> Natalia is 15 years old and is studying for her GCSEs. She is the oldest of four children. The
> youngest child is 9 months old. The family lives in a small terraced house on a busy road in the
> middle of a lively town.
>
> Although it is only a small house, Natalia has her own room, as she needs space to study. Her
> parents are very supportive of her needs and encourage her to get to bed early.

Evaluate how well Natalia is likely to sleep and whether
her sleep pattern may affect her exam results.   **(8 marks)**

Remember to include both positive
and negative effects on Natalia's sleep.
For example, she may not sleep well
because the baby may wake her, but
if she goes to bed early, she might get
enough sleep before the baby wakes.

Natalia may not sleep well because ....

....

....

Her sleep may also be disturbed by other members of

the family because she has a ....

....

....

.... She may also be woken up by ....

....

....

However, Natalia does have her own bedroom. If her room is away from the baby's

room and the noise from the street, she should be able to ....

....

....

Although her sleep pattern is likely to be disturbed and her studying may not be as effective

as it could be if she lived in a different home environment, she should ....

....

Influences on lifestyles 1

Guided 1 Jennifer is 42 years old. She lives with her husband Michael and their two teenage children. She is 12 kg heavier than she used to be, and has been feeling very depressed and self-conscious about her weight.

Describe **two** ways in which Jennifer's husband and children could help her to adopt a healthier lifestyle and lose weight. **(4 marks)**

1. The whole family could eat more healthily so Jennifer ....

....

....

....

> Think about ways the family could do something together to help Jennifer lose weight.

2. ....

....

....

2 Rosie is 12 years old. Her family are travellers. She moves around the country with her parents and brothers and sisters.

Explain **two** ways in which Rosie's culture might influence her lifestyle choices. **(4 marks)**

1. ....

....

....

....

....

> Be careful not to make any negative assumptions about a way of life that you may know nothing about. Think about general things, such as school and access to health screening.

2. ....

....

....

3 Mohammed is an observant Muslim.

State **two** ways in which his beliefs may affect the lifestyle choices he makes. **(2 marks)**

1. ....

....

2. ....

....

Influences on lifestyles 2

1 One important influence on adopting a healthy or unhealthy lifestyle is peer group pressure.

Which of the following is the definition of peer group pressure? **(1 mark)**

Put a cross in **one** box ☒ to indicate your answer.

A ☐ The pressure put on a person to do the right thing by family

B ☐ The pressure put on young people by the media

> Remember that peer pressure can be both a good and a bad influence.

C ☐ The influence that teachers have on learners

D ☐ The influence that people in a particular social group can have on other members of the group

2 Camilla is 13 years old. At the start of the summer holidays, her family moved to a new area. She is likely to be at the top of her class when she starts her new school. She has made some older friends who live on her new road. They smoke and drink alcohol, and she has started joining in.

 (a) Explain **two** ways in which negative peer pressure might influence Camilla to make some poor choices. **(4 marks)**

1. As her new friends smoke, Camilla may start to smoke so that she feels accepted in the group.

2. ....

....

(b) Identify **two** ways in which positive peer pressure might influence Camilla to make some good choices once she starts her new school. **(2 marks)**

1. ....

....

2. ....

....

Influences on lifestyles 3

1 Farrah is 10 years old. She is the oldest of five children. Her parents often tell her to behave or do things in a certain way, so she will be a good role model for her younger siblings.

(a) What is meant by the term 'role model?' **(1 mark)**

....

....

> **Guided**

(b) Give **two** ways in which Farrah might be a good role model to her siblings. **(2 marks)**

1. Farrah might have very good manners, so ....

....

....

2. Farrah might be praised for keeping her room neat

and tidy, so ....

....

> Think of a family that you know with several children. How does the oldest one influence the others?

2 Feng is 13 years old. She loves watching TV, reading magazines, surfing the internet and using social media.

(a) Identify **two** ways in which the media may influence Feng's lifestyle choices. **(2 marks)**

1. ....

....

2. ....

....

(b) Describe **two** examples of role models for Feng other than those from the media, and explain how they may influence her. **(4 marks)**

1. ....

....

....

....

....

> The question asks for two different role models, so you can use one family member as an example, but you also need to think of another type of role model.

2. ....

....

....

Influences on lifestyles 4

1 A wide range of factors can influence whether a person adopts a healthy or unhealthy lifestyle.

Which of the following is **not** an example of a factor that influences adopting a healthy or unhealthy lifestyle choice? **(1 mark)**

Put a cross in **one** box ☒ to indicate your answer.

A ☐ Self-esteem levels

B ☐ Education

C ☐ The number of holidays taken each year

D ☐ Personal and family finances

Guided

2 Read the information about Harry in the box below.

> Harry is 21 years old and has severe haemophilia. This means that, if he cuts himself, his blood will not clot as easily and he will bleed for longer than a person without the condition. He is also more likely to bleed internally around a joint after a knock, and this will lead to swollen, painful joints. Harry regularly injects himself with clotting agent and has to attend a number of medical appointments each year to monitor and deal with his condition.

Evaluate the effects of Harry's condition on his lifestyle choices. **(8 marks)**

> To help you assess a range of effects, try to think of different areas of Harry's life.

Harry will have to think carefully about the exercise or

activities he takes part in. ....

....

....

....

He will also have to think carefully about his career choices as he ....

....

....

....

He should not abuse substances that might lead him to be more careless such as ....

....

....

His personal hygiene will need to be good as he ....

....

....

Improving health and wellbeing 1

1 Ikbal is 19 years old. He lives in a damp, cold flat and is ill quite regularly. He tends to eat takeaways and drink a lot of sugary energy drinks. He used to enjoy football at school, but no longer plays.

   (a) Identify **three** areas of Ikbal's lifestyle that he could change to improve his health and wellbeing. **(3 marks)**

   1. ....

   2. ....

   3. ....

   (b) For each of the three areas, write a clear statement for Ikbal of what he needs to do to improve his lifestyle. **(3 marks)**

   > Start with 'I intend to…'

   1. ....

   2. ....

   3. ....

Guided 2 A useful tool in improving health is a health improvement plan.

   Identify **three** features of a successful health improvement plan. **(3 marks)**

   1. Benefits of meeting targets

   2. ....

   3. ....

3 Dave is 53 years old. He is divorced with three children, who live with their mother some distance away. He is often stressed and smokes 30 cigarettes a day. He also drinks most evenings, and binge drinks at the weekends.

   (a) Identify **two** areas of Dave's lifestyle that he could change to improve his health and wellbeing. **(2 marks)**

   1. ....

   2. ....

   (b) Identify **one** area of his life that Dave is not able to change at the moment. **(1 mark)**

   ....

Improving health and wellbeing 2

Guided **1** Before starting a health improvement plan it is important to recognise any difficulties that may arise and plan to overcome them.

Which **two** of the following are difficulties that may be encountered when starting and keeping to a healthy lifestyle? **(2 marks)**

Put a cross in **two** boxes ☒ to indicate your answer.

A ☒ Time commitment

B ☐ A dietician

C ☐ Being part of a supportive family

D ☐ Getting started

E ☐ Attending a slimming club

2 Mike is 21 years old. He is a professional footballer who has been injured and is not allowed to play for six months. He needs to keep fit but the non-league club he plays for only employs one trainer for the team training sessions, which Mike cannot attend.

Explain **two** difficulties Mike might face in setting out to maintain his fitness. **(4 marks)**

1. ....

....

....

2. ....

....

> Imagine yourself in the situation where you have been injured. Why would you find it hard to get started on a fitness regime?

3 Hui is 55 years old and lost his wife to cancer two years ago. He has become withdrawn from his friendship group. He goes out far less often than he used to, so he doesn't get much exercise. He has put on a lot of weight.

Give **two** excuses Hui might make for not wanting to adopt a healthier lifestyle. **(2 marks)**

1. ....

2. ....

Improving health and wellbeing 3

1 When starting a health improvement plan, it is essential to set aside time.

Explain why time commitment is an important aspect of improving health and wellbeing.

(2 marks)

....

....

2 Davinder has a desk job and often meets a friend after work for a quick drink. He decided to start running to get fit. He used to run regularly, but now says he struggles to find the time.

Explain **two** ways that Davinder could make time to go for a short run every other day.   **(4 marks)**

1. ....

....

....

....

> Think about ways in which you could fit more into your own day.

2. ....

....

Guided ▷ 3 Amber drinks a couple of glasses of wine a day. She recently started training for a half-marathon. She has decided to cut down her alcohol intake to help improve her fitness.

Describe **two** ways in which Amber could motivate herself.   **(4 marks)**

1. She could buy herself rewards, such as a new top, with the money she has saved from not drinking alcohol.

2. ....

....

Improving health and wellbeing 4

1   Health improvement targets need to be SMART.

Put a cross in **one** box ☒ for part **(a)** and **one** box for part **(b)** to indicate your answers.

(a) What does SMART stand for?   **(1 mark)**

A   ☐   Specific, Measurable, Actual, Realistic, Time-related

B   ☐   Specific, Measurable, Achievable, Reliable, Time-related

C   ☐   Specific, Meaningful, Achievable, Realistic, Time-related

D   ☐   Specific, Measurable, Achievable, Realistic, Time-related

(b) Which of the following targets is SMART?   **(1 mark)**

A   ☐   Lose 2.5 kg a week for eight weeks, starting on Monday

B   ☐   Drink less alcohol

C   ☐   Cut down on smoking a bit every week until completely stopped

D   ☐   Run for 30 minutes every Saturday and Wednesday and cycle to work three days a week

2   Joan is 51 years old. She weighs 103 kg. She is about to start a diet to lose weight. Her ideal weight for her height and age is 70 kg.

> **Guided**

(a) Write **two** SMART targets to help Joan lose weight when she starts her diet.   **(2 marks)**

| The next target needs to be more medium- or long-term. |

1.   Lose 1.5 kg in the first week.

2.   ....

(b) Write a SMART target to help Joan maintain her weight loss once she has reached her goal weight.   **(1 mark)**

....

3   Josh is 12 years old. He eats fast food every day. He goes one stop on the bus to school. He does not try very hard in PE when they do a weekly beep test.

Write **four** SMART targets to help Josh achieve a healthier lifestyle.   **(4 marks)**

1.   ....

2.   ....

3.   ....

4.   ....

Improving health and wellbeing 5

1 Reducing excessive alcohol intake is one way of improving health and wellbeing.

   (a) Suggest **one** short-term and **one** medium-term
   target for reducing alcohol intake.   **(2 marks)**

   | Short-term means for the first week or two. Medium-term means between about two and six months. |

   1. ....

   ....

   2. ....

> **Guided**

   (b) Suggest **two** short-term benefits and **two** long-term benefits of reducing alcohol intake.

                                                                            (4 marks)

   1. Short-term: *Fewer headaches/hangovers in the morning*

   2. Short-term:...

   3. Long-term:..

   4. Long-term:..

2 Jay drinks several alcoholic drinks during an evening. His wife will join him at dinner and have several glasses of wine. They eat healthily but Jay is overweight due to his alcohol consumption. His daughter is getting married, so he wants to reduce his alcohol consumption to help lose his excess weight before her wedding day. His wife has said she will do the same to support him. They sit down to write a health improvement plan to start the next week.

   (a) Explain **two** strategies they could include in the first two weeks of their health plan.

                                                                            (4 marks)

   1. ....

   ....

   ....

   2. ....

   ....

   ....

   (b) Suggest **two** alternative strategies and explain why they may be needed.   **(2 marks)**

   1. ....

   ....

   2. ....

   ....

Improving health and wellbeing 6

1 Intervention strategies, including hypnotherapy, can be used to reduce alcohol consumption or drug use, or for help when stopping smoking.

Which of the following is the definition of hypnotherapy?   **(1 mark)**

Put a cross in **one** box ☒ to indicate your answer.

A ☐ The use of pressure points in the body to overcome a problem

B ☐ The use of the power of suggestion to help overcome a problem

C ☐ The use of the power of suggestion to correct physical imbalances

D ☐ The use of touch to channel energy and restore physical and emotional wellbeing

〉**Guided**〉 2 Acupuncture is another strategy that can be used to support health improvement.

State **two** facts about acupuncture.   **(2 marks)**

1. Fine needles are inserted into the skin at certain points on the body.

2. The needles stimulate ....

....

3 Tao is 16 years old. He wants to reduce his use of recreational drugs. He sometimes steals money to buy drugs.

> If your friend were taking drugs, what would you suggest to them?

Explain **three** strategies Tao could use to reduce his drug use.   **(6 marks)**

1. ....

....

....

2. ....

....

....

3. ....

....

....

Formal support

1   Iain is 8 years old and uses a wheelchair. At school he is very shy, as his wheelchair stops him doing everything his classmates do. This worries his mother.

   (a) What is meant by 'formal support'?   **(1 mark)**

....

....

   (b) Give **two** sources of formal support that Iain's mother could use for advice.   **(2 marks)**

   1. ....

   2. ....

Guided   2   Kelly is 17 years old. She wants advice about safe sex from her doctor. Her doctor is male, but she would rather talk to a female doctor.

Explain **two** ways in which the male doctor can provide formal support for Kelly.   **(4 marks)**

> Think of different sources of support to avoid repeating yourself in your answer. For example, make sure your support isn't just based around the GP's surgery.

   1. He could ask a female doctor or a practice nurse to have a chat with her to ....

....

....

   2. ....

....

....

3   Elaine is 58 years old. She has recently been diagnosed with arthritis. Her condition isn't helped by the fact that she is overweight.

Identify **three** sources of formal support Elaine could access to help her with her problems.

                                                                      (3 marks)

   1. ....

   2. ....

   3. ....

Informal support

1 Beryl is 86 years old and, apart from having arthritis, she is fit, active and in good health. She lives in sheltered accommodation where there is a warden to look out for her and the other residents. She still does everything for herself except for her supermarket shopping, as she no longer drives and it is too far to walk.

Beryl's friend Harold, who lives next door, pops in most mornings for a coffee and chat. Her children and grandchildren visit her regularly, taking it in turns to drive her to the supermarket. Her friend Mabel, whom she worked with for 30 years, will often visit.

(a) Describe **two** sources of informal support available to Beryl. **(4 marks)**

1. ....

....

2. ....

....

> As you need to 'describe' the support, think about how each source helps Beryl.

Recently, Beryl's eyesight has started to worsen and her arthritis has become more painful.

> **Guided**

(b) What extra help will Beryl's sources of informal support be able to give her to improve her health and wellbeing? **(4 marks)**

1. They could give her lifts to appointments with the doctors/optician.

2. They could help her read her post and deal with it (for example, help her pay her bills).

3. ....

....

....

4. ....

....

> To gain all the marks and avoid repetition in your answer, give one answer for each separate need (that is: physical, intellectual, emotional and social). So far, there are answers for physical and intellectual. Try and think of one for emotional and one for social.

Support in maintaining positive change

1 Informal support is essential for maintaining lifestyle changes.

Which of the following is **not** a form of support? **(1 mark)**

Put a cross in **one** box ☒ to indicate your answer.

A ☐ Listening

B ☐ Empathy

C ☐ Criticism

D ☐ Encouragement

2 Julie is obese. She is following a health improvement plan to lose weight, but her progress has slowed down. She is feeling disheartened and bored with her diet.

(a) Explain what Julie may do as a result of her negative feelings. **(2 marks)**

....

....

(b) Explain **two** ways in which a friend or support group could help her. **(4 marks)**

1. ....

....

....

2. ....

....

....

Guided

3 Andrew has given up smoking. He is still craving cigarettes.

Describe **two** sources of support that could help Andrew. **(4 marks)**

> Pick one formal and one informal source to make sure that you give two different answers.

1. An organisation that supports smokers who are giving up could provide ....

....

2. He could ask his work colleagues who don't smoke to ....

....

Barriers to health 1

1 George is happily married with two teenage children. He wants to regain his fitness level, so he has been paying for regular sessions with a personal trainer at the local gym to make him commit the time and give him motivation. He has just found out that his wife is pregnant. He is worried about the cost of buying new things for the baby, so has cancelled his gym sessions.

> Guided

(a) Explain **two** barriers to George continuing to improve his fitness.   **(4 marks)**

> A barrier in this case is some part of a person's life that stops them doing what they need to do to become healthier.

1. George can no longer afford ....
....

....

2. George will find it harder to find time to commit to fitness, because ....
....

....

(b) Describe **two** ways in which George can overcome these barriers.   **(4 marks)**

1. ....

....

2. ....

....

2 Perry is 16 years old and has learning difficulties, which means he is easily persuaded to do things. He has started smoking as a result of peer pressure. He tried to get advice from the school nurse before he started smoking, but she was not available at the time.

Identify **two** barriers to Perry stopping smoking.   **(2 marks)**

1. ....

....

....

2. ....

....

....

Barriers to health 2

1   Clare is 58 years old. She has just had a total knee replacement. Her recovery will be a slow process – at the moment she is weak, in pain and unable to walk without crutches. It will be six weeks before she is off crutches. None of her friends or family can help her go for a walk during the day. After struggling with her weight, last year she managed to reach her ideal weight by briskly walking every day and eating healthily. She has a lot of friends visiting her, and they often bring her chocolates.

> **Guided**

(a) Explain **two** possible barriers Clare may currently have to maintaining a healthy lifestyle.

(4 marks)

> The case study talks about her knee and her weight, so find a barrier for each.

   1.   Clare cannot go for a walk on her own during the day because ....

   ....

   ....

   2.   Clare's friends bring her chocolates, which ....

   ....

   ....

(b) Describe **two** ways in which these barriers could be overcome.   **(4 marks)**

   1.   ....

   ....

   2.   ....

   ....

2   Naomi is 15 years old. She dreams of becoming a model and reads lots of fashion magazines. Her mother is worried that Naomi is too thin and tries to get her to eat more by tempting her with her favourite junk food.

   Identify **two** barriers Naomi may have to leading a healthy lifestyle.   **(2 marks)**

   1.   ....

   2.   ....

Barriers to health 3

1 Belinda is 28 years old. She is obese. She sweats heavily and gets out of breath easily when exercising, so she just gives up. She has recently lost her job and thinks she is a failure.

Give **two** factors that may limit Belinda's achievement of a healthy lifestyle. **(2 marks)**

1. ....

2. ....

> **Guided**

2 Read the information about Nigel in the box below.

> Nigel is 44 years old and until recently, he was very fit and healthy. He used to run regularly and play in a football team with his friends. He works as a computer repairman. Without any warning he had a stroke, which has left him unable to move his left arm and leg, and the left-hand side of his face droops.
>
> His doctors have told Nigel that he will get some movement back in his leg, but he will have a limp and have to walk with a stick. His face will return to normal, but it is unlikely his arm will.
>
> For the moment, he will have to stay in hospital to be monitored. He will then be moved to a rehabilitation ward, to learn how to cope with his disability and do everyday tasks. It will take about a year until he is fully able to do things for himself. He will need to continue to have physiotherapy after that.
>
> Nigel is very depressed and often asks himself what he has done to deserve this.

Evaluate the likelihood of Nigel achieving a healthy lifestyle in two years' time. **(8 marks)**

> When you are asked to **evaluate**, it is important to give both positive and negative points so you offer a balanced argument.

Nigel will find it very hard to ....

....

....

....

> Remember PIES when answering this question.

....

....

However, Nigel may decide he doesn't want to be beaten by this setback. He will ....

....

....

....

....

....

If Nigel adopts a positive attitude ....

....

....

Barriers to health 4

Guided 1 Read the information about Magnus in the box below.

> Magnus is 30 years old. He is homeless and lives on the streets. He didn't do very well at school, as he often truanted with his friends. He spent the money his parents gave him on cigarettes and junk food. He eventually became addicted to drugs.
>
> Although he beat his addiction a couple of years ago, he no longer has contact with his parents, as he stole from them to buy drugs. He also lost his job and home due to his drug habit.
>
> He is not happy with himself and has decided to make some major changes. He would like to work so he can afford to rent somewhere to live, but he cannot find anyone who will give him a job.
>
> His only friends are other homeless people. Although he has lost contact with his family, he knows they loved him very much and would be delighted if he had changed his ways.

Evaluate the likelihood of Magnus turning his life around and achieving a healthy lifestyle.

(8 marks)

In order to adopt a healthy lifestyle, Magnus will need help. He could seek help from ....

....

....

....

....

....

....

....

....

However, Magnus may find it hard to ....

....

....

....

....

....

....

....

If Magnus is determined enough, ...

....

....

Exam skills 1

 1 The information in Table A shows details of Simone's height and weight.

Height (in m)	Weight (in kg)
1.6	45

Table A

Calculate Simone's Body Mass Index (BMI) to one decimal place. **(2 marks)**

$$BMI = \frac{(\text{Weight in kg})}{(\text{Height in metres})^2}$$

BMI = ... kg/m²

$$BMI = \frac{45}{\underset{2}{\text{.........................}}}$$

> Show your workings out.

> The first thing you need to do is multiply the height by itself before doing the division. Remember, you should be dividing a bigger number by a smaller number.

2 The information in Table A shows details of Tom's height and weight.

Height (in m)	Weight (in kg)
2.1	120

Table A

Calculate Tom's Body Mass Index (BMI) to one decimal place. **(2 marks)**

$$BMI = \frac{(\text{Weight in kg})}{(\text{Height in metres})^2}$$

BMI = ... kg/m²

....

....

....

....

Exam skills 2

BMI	Rating
<19	Underweight
20–25	Desirable
26–30	Overweight
31+	Obese

Table A

1   Using Simone's BMI result from page 75, select her BMI rating using Table A.   **(1 mark)**

Put a cross in one box ☒ to indicate your answer. If you change your mind, put a line through the box ☒ and then put a cross in another box ☒.

Rating

A ☐ Underweight

B ☐ Desirable

C ☐ Overweight

D ☐ Obese

2   Using Tom's BMI result from page 75, select his BMI rating using Table A.   **(1 mark)**

Put a cross in one box ☒ to indicate your answer. If you change your mind, put a line through the box ☒ and then put a cross in another box ☒.

Rating

A ☐ Underweight

B ☐ Desirable

C ☐ Overweight

D ☐ Obese

Exam skills 3

Objective questions

1 Drinking alcohol in moderation can be beneficial to health.

State **one** long-term health risk associated with drinking excessively. **(1 mark)**

....

....

> Objective questions need a short but accurate answer. You are not expected to explain anything; just give, state or identify, a brief answer. These questions are usually worth one mark, but may be worth two if you need to give more than one point.

Short answer questions

2 Jasmine is 15 years old and overweight. She enjoys going out with her school friends. Her friends are worried that every year she is putting on a bit more weight.

Explain **two** ways in which Jasmine's friends can use peer pressure to help her lose weight. **(4 marks)**

> Answers to these questions need more explanation and earn you more marks. They ask you to explain or describe.

1. ....

....

....

2. ....

....

....

 3 Colin is 88 years old and lives in a residential care home. He is very sociable.

Identify **one** positive effect on Colin's social wellbeing of living in a residential care home.

(1 mark)

Colin will have company in the form of ....

....

....

Exam skills 4

Guided   1   Read the information about Shirley in the box below.

> Shirley is 52 years old and works as a secondary school maths teacher. During the week, her evenings are spent marking and preparing lessons. The thought of having a couple of glasses of wine as a reward motivates her to get through it.
>
> She has always been overweight, despite going to the gym and swimming twice a week. She enjoys eating out and going for regular weekends away. She often goes away to a holiday cottage with her husband and their two children. There they often eat out to save her having to cook and to make it a relaxing break.
>
> Recently, at her annual health check at her GP's surgery, Shirley was told that her blood pressure was too high. She was advised to lose 19 kg in weight over the next six months to bring her blood pressure down to an acceptable level.

Evaluate the likelihood of Shirley achieving this goal.

(8 marks)

> You are expected to write a much more detailed answer, which should give a balance of positive and negative points, and then a conclusion. You need to write in proper sentences and take care with spelling, punctuation and grammar so that your answer is very clear.

Shirley has a busy job. She may find it hard to give up her ....

....

....

....

....

....

....

....

However, Shirley is an intelligent person and knows what she needs to do to help herself.

Instead of having a couple of glasses of wine to relax every night, she could ....

....

....

....

....

....

Overall, Shirley has .... chance of achieving her goal if she

....

....

Unit 1: Practice assessment test

You have 1 hour to complete this test.

The total number of marks is 50.

Instructions

- Use **black** ink or ballpoint pen.
- Answer **all** questions.
- Answer the questions in the spaces provided.

1   The following information is about the Evans family.
Read the information and answer the questions below.

> Brian is 42 years old and lives with his partner Liz, who is 39. They have three children. Marc is 13, Kate is 4 and Ross is 12 months.
>
> Brian works full time as a lorry driver. Liz stays at home caring for the children.

(a) Identify the current life stages of Brian and Marc below.   **(2 marks)**

Draw lines to match Brian and Marc to their current life stage.

Names	Life stages
	Early childhood
Brian	
	Adolescence
	Early adulthood
Marc	Middle adulthood
	Later adulthood

> Kate likes her father to read her a story book at bedtime.

(b) What type of development are story books **most** important for?   **(1 mark)**

Put a cross in **one** box ☒ to indicate your answer.

A ☐ Physical development

B ☐ Intellectual development

C ☐ Emotional development

D ☐ Social development

Marc and Kate go to school, but Ross stays at home with his mother, Liz. Ross has formed a strong attachment with Liz and is unhappy if he is left with other people.

(c) Outline what is meant by the term 'attachment'. **(1 mark)**

....

Liz wants to help Ross in developing his intellectual skills.

(d) (i) Give **two** intellectual skills that Ross is likely to be developing at his life stage. **(2 marks)**

1. ....

2. ....

(ii) For each intellectual skill, give an example of an activity that could be used to develop the skill. **(2 marks)**

Complete the table below.

Intellectual skill	Activity

At school, Kate likes to play dressing-up with her friend.

The image shows a child playing dressing-up.

(e) Give **two** possible effects of social play on Kate's development. **(2 marks)**

1. ....

....

....

....

2. ....

....

....

....

Marc is good at athletics. He has just been selected to represent his school in the area athletics competition.

(f) Give **two** possible effects of being selected for the competition on Marc's emotional development. **(2 marks)**

1. ....

2. ....

Marc is just beginning puberty.

(g) Identify **two** physical changes that Marc will experience at this life stage. **(2 marks)**

1. ....

2. ....

Liz has to go into hospital for two weeks to have an operation on her back. While she is in hospital, the children will be cared for by their aunt.

(h) (i) Explain **two** possible effects of going into hospital on Liz's development. **(4 marks)**

1. ....

....

2. ....

....

(ii) Explain **one** negative effect and **one** positive effect on Ross's development of his mother going into hospital. **(4 marks)**

Positive ....

....

Negative ....

....

(Total for question 1 = 22 marks)

2   The following information is about Rafal and Micha.
Read the information and answer the questions below.

> Rafal is 47 years old and divorced. He lives with his son Micha, who is 22. Rafal works full time as a teacher and has recently been promoted to Head of Year. He likes to keep himself fit, so he has joined a local gym. His marriage ended last year, when Rafal got divorced from his wife Lena.

(a) (i)   Identify **one** expected life event and **one** unexpected life event that Rafal has experienced. **(2 marks)**

Expected life event: ....

Unexpected life event: ....

(ii)   Give **two** ways in which divorce could have affected Rafal's development. **(2 marks)**

1. ....

2. ....

(iii)   Give **two** positive effects of regular exercise on Rafal's growth and development. **(2 marks)**

1. ....

2. ....

> Micha has Down's syndrome, a genetically inherited disorder. He can manage his own personal care, but is still reliant on his father for many of his needs. Micha and Rafal are supported by a voluntary organisation for people with Down's syndrome. Micha attends a training centre for young adults with learning disabilities.

(b) (i)   Give **two** specific types of support that the voluntary organisation might give to help Micha and his father. **(2 marks)**

1. ....

2. ....

(ii) Explain **two** possible effects of Micha's genetic disorder on his growth and development.

(4 marks)

1. ....

....

2. ....

....

(iii) Explain **two** possible effects of his son's genetic disorder on Rafal's development.

(4 marks)

1. ....

....

2. ....

....

Rafal has developed a close relationship with Maia, who he met at work. He has asked her to move in with him.

(c) Explain **two** possible effects of his new relationship on Rafal's emotional and social development.

(4 marks)

1. ....

....

2. ....

....

> The training centre that Micha attends has organised a two-week holiday for him and other young adults. They will stay in a hostel where they will help with everyday tasks such as cooking and cleaning. Micha will be able to take part in walking and sailing activities. This will be the first time that he has been away from Rafal for longer than a weekend.

(d) Assess the possible impact to Micha's growth and development of attending this type of holiday and how his time away will affect Rafal's growth and development. **(8 marks)**

....
....
....
....
....
....
....
....
....
....
....
....
....
....
....
....
....
....
....
....
....
....
....
....
....
....

(Total for question 2 = 28 marks)

Unit 9: Practice assessment test

You have 1 hour to complete this test.
The total number of marks is 50.

Instructions

- Use **black** ink or ballpoint pen.
- Answer **all** questions.
- Answer the questions in the spaces provided.

1   Personal hygiene is an important part of a healthy lifestyle.

    (a) Give **two** effects of poor personal hygiene.   **(2 marks)**

    1. ....

    2. ....

    (b) Give **one** way in which obesity can have a negative effect on personal hygiene.   **(1 mark)**

    ....

2   It is important to have regular sleep as part of a healthy lifestyle.

    (a) Which **two** of the following may result from a lack of sleep?   **(2 marks)**

    Put a cross in **two** boxes ☒ to indicate your answer.

    A ☐ Weight gain

    B ☐ Fatigue

    C ☐ Accidents

    D ☐ Better concentration

    E ☐ Increased productivity

    (b) State **one** health risk associated with a lack of sleep.   **(1 mark)**

    ....

3   A good work/life balance is important for good health and wellbeing.

    (a) Which **one** of the following is the definition of a good work/life balance?   **(1 mark)**

    Put a cross in **one** box ☒ to indicate your answer.

    A ☐ Being motivated by work with little time for a social life

    B ☐ Long hours at work to earn lots of money

    C ☐ Taking work home in the evenings

    D ☐ Regularly leaving work on time to spend time with family and friends

(b) Explain **two** reasons why a good work/life balance is important. **(4 marks)**

1. ....

....

2. ....

....

4   Eating a balanced diet is an important part of maintaining a healthy lifestyle.

Give **two** benefits of eating a balanced diet. **(2 marks)**

1. ....

2. ....

5   Christopher is 14 years old and is overweight. He sometimes sneaks out of school at lunchtime and spends his dinner money on fast food.

Describe how peer pressure could help Christopher lose weight. **(2 marks)**

....

....

6   The information in Table A shows some details of Christine's height and weight.

Height (in m)	Weight (in kg)
1.8	58

Table A

(a) Calculate Christine's Body Mass Index (BMI). **(2 marks)**

$$BMI = \frac{\text{Weight in kg}}{(\text{Height in m})^2}$$

....

....

BMI = ... kg/m²

(b) Using Christine's BMI result, select her correct BMI rating using Table B. **(1 mark)**

BMI	Rating
<19	Underweight
20–25	Desirable
26–30	Overweight
31+	Obese

Table B

Rating		
A	☐	Underweight
B	☐	Desirable
C	☐	Overweight
D	☐	Obese

7 Intellectual wellbeing is as important as physical health and emotional and social wellbeing.

Explain **two** ways in which lifestyle choices can have a positive effect on intellectual wellbeing.

(4 marks)

1. ....

....

2. ....

....

8 Using recreational drugs is a risk to health and wellbeing.

Explain **two** ways in which taking drugs may affect health and wellbeing.   **(4 marks)**

1. ....

....

2. ....

....

9 Drinking in moderation can have positive effects on health.

(a) State **two** benefits to health of drinking alcohol.   **(2 marks)**

1. ....

2. ....

(b) Explain **two** ways in which drinking alcohol can affect health and wellbeing.   **(4 marks)**

1. ....

....

2. ....

....

(c) Give **two** sources of formal support available for help with cutting down alcohol consumption.   **(2 marks)**

1. ....

2. ....

10 Richard is 57 years old and has smoked since the age of 12. He would like to retire from his stressful job, but cannot afford to do this yet. He has been advised by his doctor to stop smoking.

Explain **two** possible barriers that Richard may have in giving up smoking.   **(4 marks)**

1. ....

....

2. ....

....

11 Nicky is a single mother. She is on a very low income. She lives with her five-year-old daughter Carmel in a small flat on the ninth floor of a building. The lift is often not working.

Explain **two** possible barriers that Carmel may have to achieving a healthy lifestyle.   **(4 marks)**

1. ....

....

2. ....

....

12 Read the information about Lance in the box below.

> Lance is 63 years old and is happily married with four children. His children now have their own homes and families, but keep in regular contact. Lance retired from teaching ten years ago. He has many interests including hill walking, cycling and being a member of the local mountain rescue team.
>
> Last year he had heart problems and although he had an operation, he has lost much of his fitness. He has also put on about 13 kg in weight. He is worried that if he goes back to doing the activities he did before, he may have a heart attack. His doctor has assured him that this is very unlikely to happen.
>
> Lance has decided to try to get back to his former fitness. He has set himself a target of being able to cycle ten miles in two months' time.

Evaluate the likelihood of Lance achieving this goal.   **(8 marks)**

....

....

....

....

....

....

....

....

....

Answers

The following pages contain example answers for questions in the Workbook. In many cases, they represent only one possible correct answer.

UNIT 1 ANSWERS

LEARNING AIM A

1. The six life stages

1 (a) 1. Ruby is in the early childhood life stage.

2. Sara is in the early adulthood life stage.

(b) **D** Later adulthood

(c) 9–18 years

2. Aspects of development

1 (a) Emotional development is the development of feelings about self and others.

(b) Intellectual development

(c) Playing cricket: physical development

Studying a language: intellectual development

3. Growth and physiological change

1 (a) Growth is an increase in size, such as height, head circumference or weight. Growth can be measured. Physiological change is a physical change that happens to the human body at the different life stages.

(b) Jane: Has started the menopause

Reece: Has reached physical maturity

Toby: Is experiencing a growth spurt

Bill: Has lost some muscle tone

4. Gross motor skills

1 (a) Any two from: balancing/walking along a line; running up steps; climbing; riding a tricycle; throwing.

(b) Any two from: playing with sit-on toys; playing with push-along toys; action songs that use the arms; baby swing; rolling a large ball; crawling.

(c) 1. Climbing on the frame will strengthen the muscles in Aidan's arms and legs because he will use them to push and pull his body along the frame.

2. Aidan will develop coordination when bouncing on the trampoline because he will need to use the large muscles in his whole body to help his balance.

5. Fine motor skills

1 (a) Fine motor skills are skills needed to control the small muscles in the body and hands. Gross motor skills are skills needed to control the large muscles in the body, the arms and the legs.

(b) **B** Finger painting **D** Feeding self

(c) Any two from: hand–eye coordination when placing a block on top of the tower; manipulation when he turns the block around to put it on top of the tower; grasping/gripping to lift up the brick.

6. Physical development in adolescence

1 (a) A growth spurt is when a young person grows more quickly than usual over a short period of time.

(b) **C** From 18 to 20

(c) Any two from: uterus/vagina grows; ovulation/menstruation begins.

(d) Any two from: enlargement of breasts; growth of hair in armpits/pubic hair; increased fat layers under the skin; growth spurt.

7. Physical development in adulthood

1 (a) 1. The ending of menstruation.

2. Shrinkage of sexual organs.

(b) 1. Robert may find that moving and bending down to garden is more difficult because he has lost some of his mobility and his joints have become more stiff.

2. Robert may find that he has less strength because he has lost some of his muscle tone.

8. Intellectual development

1 (a) Any two from: loss of memory/may be more difficult to recall information; his thinking speed may be reduced; he may have dementia.

(b) Any two from: learning a new skill such as a language or carpentry; doing puzzles (for example, crosswords, number puzzles, jigsaws); socialising with friends.

2 (a) Caden should have developed a wide vocabulary. This will help him to understand the information that the teacher gives him in lessons and when he needs to take part in discussions. Caden will have developed skills to help him to think creatively and use abstract thought processes. These skills will help him to learn new concepts and ideas in science lessons. When Caden is given maths tasks to work out, he will be able to use his problem-solving skills to help him to work out the answers. He should have well-developed memory and recall skills. These are important for answering questions in class or during tests and examinations.

9. Language development

1 (a) (i) Noah: Can read independently

Chloe: Knows around 50 words

Ryan: Is beginning to ask questions

Maggie: Understands words such as 'bye bye'

(ii) Any two from: action rhymes/songs; picture books; puppet play.

(b) 1. Playing with other children will help Ryan to develop his speaking and listening skills.

2. Listening to stories and rhymes will help Ryan to develop and extend his vocabulary.

10. Moral development

1 (a) Moral development describes the development of the values that we hold and the principles that we live by, and an understanding of how to treat others.

(b) 1. Playing a simple board game and taking turns.

2. Getting Milek to hand out sweets or biscuits to other children to encourage sharing.

(c) Adolescents are developing their own ideas about right and wrong, and are therefore beginning to question the moral values of others.

11. Emotional development

1 (a) **Positive:**

One from: she is happy with her own appearance; she gets positive comments from others (her friends).

Negative:

One from: she may compare herself unfavourably with friends; she may compare herself with celebrities in the media/magazines.

2 (a) 1. Natalie may have high self-esteem because she is in a good relationship/part of a couple.

2. Natalie may feel more secure because she and Mark now have their own home.

(b) Any two from: Mark may have low self-esteem because he feels worthless/does not value himself because he has no job; Mark may be stressed because he has lost his income and is worried about paying the mortgage, bills and other expenses; Mark may be less contented because his lifestyle will have to change as he has less money; Mark may have low self-esteem because he feels that he has to rely on Natalie.

12. Social development

1 (a) Independence is being able to make your own decisions, do things for yourself and not having to rely on others.

(b) Any two from: Maya may build formal relationships because she has to discuss her college work with her teachers; Maya may build new friendships and learn to value others because she will be meeting new people on her course; Maya may develop independence because she will need to make decisions and do things for herself.

(c) One from: Yasir may be able to build new relationships with his new colleagues; Yasir may socialise with new people living nearby and build new friendships; Yasir may gain more independence by learning new skills in his new job.

(d) One from: Yasir may be unable to maintain social relationships because he has moved away from friends and family; Yasir may feel more isolated and find it difficult to build new friendships.

13. Emotional and social development in infancy

1 (a) Logan: Has a strong attachment with parent or main carer.
Bella: Is dependent on parents but is beginning to form bonds with others.

(b) Bonding and attachment describe the close relationship that infants develop from birth with parents or carers.

(c) Any two from: Leon will learn how to build friendships with other children because he will take part in social play and group activities; Leon will become less reliant on his mother, which will help him to develop more independence; Leon is being cared for by Emma and other adults at the nursery, and will therefore learn how to build relationships with people outside his own family.

14. Emotional and social development in early childhood

1 (a) Any two from: he is forming relationships with adults other than his parents (teachers); he is developing independence (he is able to do things for himself, and is not relying on others for his needs); he is developing special friendships/he may have a special friend; he is developing a wider circle of friends.

(b) Grace's emotional development will progress when she starts school as she will need to develop attachments with other people outside her own home, such as her teachers and lunchtime supervisors.
Grace may feel unhappy because the routines and people at the school will be new/unfamiliar to her. This could have a negative effect on her emotional development because she may feel insecure.

Playing with other children will help her social development, as she will learn how to share and build friendships and may develop a special friendship.
She will not have her mum there to help her with everyday tasks, so she will learn to become more independent, which may help Grace's confidence to grow.

15. Emotional and social development in adolescence

1 (a) (i) 1. Lauren may not feel good about the way she looks.
2. Arguing with her parents may make Lauren feel insecure/confused.

(ii) A Lauren may be reluctant to go out and meet friends
D Lauren may not want to take part in after-school activities

(b) One from: Theo may have high self-esteem because he has done well in his exams/has been given a place at college; Theo may feel contented because he has achieved his goals at school and has secured a place on a course that he wants to do.

(c) One from: Theo will have the opportunity to develop new friendship groups with the people he meets at college; Theo will need to build formal relationships with teachers and others he meets at college; Theo will develop independence as he is leaving school and starting college, and entering a new phase in his life.

16. Emotional and social development in adulthood

1 (a) Any two from: high self-esteem; feels more contented at work; has a positive self-image; feels more secure.

(b) **Positive:**
Zoe may develop a closer relationship with Madiha because they will have more time to spend together when Gemma moves away.
Negative:
Zoe may experience anxiety because she worries that she may lose the close relationship she had with Gemma when she moves abroad.

(c) Any two from: unable to maintain relationships with friends; may lose the close bond she has with Madiha; will lose independence; will have fewer opportunities to build new friendships/relationships.

LEARNING AIM B

17. Genetic inheritance

1 (a) Genetic inheritance is the passing of genes from parents to children and how these genes influence their physical features, characteristics and development.

(b) A Eye colour C Height

2 (a) Any two from: the disorder may affect Ava's intellectual development if she has to miss college because she is ill; the disorder may affect Ava's ability to build close friendships because needing to have regular physiotherapy and illness means that she has less time to socialise; Ava may develop a negative self-image because she often feels unwell; Ava's physical development (growth/weight) may be delayed because the disorder may affect her digestive system.

18. Lifestyle choices

1 (a) 1. Drinking too much alcohol may affect Demaine's social development because it could cause a breakdown in his relationship with Paula.

2. Drinking too much alcohol may affect Demaine's intellectual development because it may make it more difficult for Demaine to think or make decisions.

(b) Any two from: a healthy diet will promote growth because it is made up of foods that contain all the nutrients the body needs; a healthy diet will improve skin and hair, which will improve self-image; improved self-image will lead to improved self-confidence, which helps in developing friendships/relationships; a healthy diet will result in better health so individuals are more able to take part in different activities, which leads to more independence.

(c) Any two from: an unhealthy diet can cause problems with physical development because it can cause illnesses, such as heart disease/diabetes; an unhealthy diet can cause weight gain, which puts increased pressure on the joints and this can affect mobility (for example, from arthritis); an unhealthy diet may cause weight gain/ obesity, which may result in a negative self-image.

19. Illness and disease

1 (a) **B** Physical development

(b) Any two from: loss of independence; unable to meet friends; loss of mobility; feeling anxious; being worried about the future.

(c) Any two from: Nadia may not have as much time for socialising/building friendships as she is spending time caring for her mother; Nadia may feel stressed because she is worried about her mother's health; Nadia may be unable to function as well at work because she is anxious about her mother's health; Nadia may not care as much about her own appearance because she is concerned about her mother.

20. The influence of play

1 (a) **B** Speech and vocabulary

(b) In solitary play, children play alone or alongside others, but in social play, they join in play with other children.

(c) Amir: Drama; musical instruments; painting
Humayra: Play dough; painting
Timmy: Finger/hand painting

21. Culture

1 Any two from: Ellen will develop friendships with other Christians at her church; Ellen's beliefs will help her to feel more contented; Ellen's beliefs will promote her self-image; being a member of the church will give Ellen a feeling of security.

2 Having people from their home country living close by will help Georgi and Tanja to build friendships. Having people from their home country living close by may also mean that they feel happier and more confident, as they share the same values. They are likely to feel more secure and contented with people who speak the same language and who have the same cultural needs. They have both secured jobs in the UK, which is likely to boost their self-esteem because others have recognised their abilities.

Georgi and Tanja could face discrimination because their culture is different to that of the majority of people in the area. This may cause them to feel stressed or anxious, which may affect their ability to work effectively. Lack of acceptance because of their culture may put a strain on their relationship with each other. If other people do not understand Georgi and Tanja's culture and values, the couple may find it difficult to develop a wider circle of friends.

22. Gender

1 Gender inequality is when individuals are treated differently because of their gender.

2 Any two from: inequality in pay; inequality of employment opportunities; social inequality such as social status of males and females; differences in gender roles; different expectations of males and females.

3 Any two from: Oliver may feel unhappy/stressed because he does not feel that his parents are supporting him; Oliver has less interest in other subjects, so not being allowed to study dance and drama may affect his ability to learn new skills; Oliver may develop a negative self-image because he has been discriminated against/told that the course he wants to take is not suitable for boys; Oliver may find it more difficult to build friendships on a course where he does not share the same interests as others; Oliver will be less contented because he cannot follow his interests.

23. Role models and social isolation

1 (a) 1. Hayley can demonstrate how to share and take turns.
   2. Hayley can show respect when speaking to Abbie and others.

2 (a) Social isolation is when people do not have regular contact with others.

(b) Any two from: Vera may feel insecure because she has no one with whom she can discuss her worries; stress and anxiety caused by social isolation may cause a decline in Vera's mental ability, such as loss of memory; Vera may adopt an unhealthy lifestyle (for example, taking up smoking or drinking excessive alcohol) because she has lost contact with friends, which would affect her health; Vera may have lost confidence in building new friendships/relationships because she feels excluded; Vera may experience physical health problems because of stress or anxiety.

24. Economic factors

1 (a) 1. Seema may feel guilty about not being able to contribute to the household bills, which may put pressure on their relationship.
   2. Seema may respond differently towards Scott because she is stressed/anxious about losing her status and income.

(b) One from: Seema's self-esteem may increase because she feels happy that she has been given a job; Seema may feel more secure because she is earning an income to pay towards the household bills; Seema's relationship with Scott may improve because she feels more contented/less anxious.

(c) One from: Seema may have negative self-image because her new job has less status than that of an accounts manager; Seema may feel insecure/stressed because she is earning much less than before and it may not be enough to pay for the household bills; Seema may not be able to afford to go out and socialise because she has less money to spend.

25. Physical environment

1 Any two from: breathing problems; asthma; heart conditions; cancers.

2 (a) 1. Kath may feel stressed because she does not have any space to relax and can't get away from the family.
   2. Kath may be more susceptible to infection because they are living on top of one another/in very close proximity.

(b) Any two from: John and Kyle will have space to play outdoors, which will help the development of their gross motor skills; John and Kyle are likely to be healthier, as they will get more rest and sleep in their own rooms; John and Kyle will be more able to learn if they are healthy; John and Kyle may feel more secure and contented, as Kath will be less stressed.

26. Family relationships

1 (a) 1. Nasim's parents are proud of his achievements.
2. Nasim has a good relationship with his parents and brother.

(b) 1. The love and support from his family will enable Nasim to become independent.
2. As Nasim has a good relationship with his family, he is more likely to be able to build and develop good relationships with others.

(c) Any two from: Omar may have low self-esteem because he has received negative comments from his parents; Omar may have a negative self-image because he may compare himself with his brother; Omar may have more difficulty building relationships with others because he is worried that these may break down; Omar may be stressed/have difficulty dealing with his emotions because he feels rejected/let down by his family.

27. Friendships and relationships

1 (a) 1. As most of his time is spent caring for Sally, Graham may not have any time to follow his own interests and meet new people.
2. The relationship between Graham and Sally may break down as Graham may become stressed because he has a full-time job to do as well as caring for Sally.

(b) Any two from: Alfie may develop a positive self-image; Alfie may feel happy and contented; Alfie may feel secure in the relationship.

28. Stress

1 (a) Any two from: Kesh wil be worried about his dad's health; pressure at work to meet high sales targets; pressure to visit/support his dad; balancing time between his family, his dad and his job.

(b) Any two from: Kesh may develop a negative self-image because he feels that he is failing at work when he compares himself with colleagues who are meeting their sales targets; Kesh may feel a lack of security because he is concerned that he might lose his father due to his heart problems; Kesh may have low self-esteem as he is getting criticism from his boss at work for not meeting his sales targets; Kesh may feel a loss of contentment in his present situation because he is unable to give time to his family as well as working and visiting his father.

29. Expected life events 1

1 (a) 1. Starting nursery
2. Starting school

(b) Any two from: leaving school; starting college or university; moving house/location; starting a new job; living with a partner; marriage or civil partnership; parenthood; retirement.

(c) Any two from: starting education (nursery, school, college, university); starting a new job; marriage; parenthood.

30. Expected life events 2

1 (a) **Positive:** Feeling of security and contentment
Negative: Loss of independence

(b) Any two from:
• Sacha may develop a sense of contentment and wellbeing, because she will have feelings of love/ strong emotional attachments to the new baby.
• She may lose her independence because she cannot take part in as many social activities as before now that she has to care for the baby.
• She may develop a closer relationship with Phil because they share the happiness and contentment of having the baby.
• She may feel anxious and stressed because she is worried about caring for the new baby.

31. Unexpected life events 1

1 (a) Expected life events are events that happen to most people during the course of their life.
Unexpected life events are events that only happen to some people. They can't be predicted.

(b) **Sylvia:**
1. She was bereaved/her son died.
2. She was made redundant from her job.

(c) **Malcolm:**
1. He was bereaved/his son died.
2. He had an accident/broke his hip.

32. Unexpected life events 2

1 (a) Any two from: exclusion may damage the relationship between Sean and his mum; Sean's mum may feel embarrassed by him being excluded; Sean's mum may feel reluctant to meet with other people as she is embarrassed that Sean has been excluded; Sean's exclusion may cause his mum to feel stressed/unwell.

(b) Sean's social development may be affected because he will no longer have informal or formal social contact with friends and teachers. His friends may reject him because of his actions. This may affect how Sean feels about himself and may result in him developing a negative self-image.
His mother is likely to be upset and angry, which may cause a breakdown in their relationship, and this could affect Sean's feeling of security.
As Sean will be missing classes, his intellectual development will be affected. He may lose skills in problem-solving and thinking. If Sean is not able to take part in the physical activities that happen at school, his gross motor skills may also be affected, as he could lose some of his fitness and agility.

33. Types of support

1 (a) **A** Formal **D** Physical
2 (a) **Formal:** one from: physical check-up or medication.
Informal: reassurance or help with everyday tasks.

(b) 1. Discussing Tia's progress with a health visitor will reassure Lisa that she is giving the care Tia needs.
2. Having a friend to listen to her and share her worries about Qas's health will help Lisa to understand and come to terms with his illness.

34. Managing change 1

1 (a) Any two from: give/monitor medication; give advice to Nadine and Glen about her condition; liaise with other health professionals, such as the physiotherapist, to help mobility.

(b) Any two from: help with coming to terms with changes in her health; help with independence or giving reassurance.

(c) 1. Anna may help Nadine to feel more positive about herself because Nadine will take more interest in her appearance when going out to meet friends.

2. Anna may help Nadine to come to terms with her illness because she is listening to her worries and giving reassurance.

35. Managing change 2

1 Religious groups give support and advice relating to health and welfare based on the beliefs and values of a particular faith.

2 1. A voluntary cancer organisation may help Sonia to make decisions about her illness because they will be able to give her specific information about the type of cancer and the treatment that is available.

2. Volunteers who work for the organisation are more likely to be able to help Sonia come to terms with her illness because they understand how she feels.

36. Exam skills 1

1 (a) Medina: Early adulthood
Carrie: Early childhood

(b) Any two from:
  • Medina may develop a positive self-image because she is earning money that will support the family/feels that her status has improved as she has a job
  • Medina's cognitive/intellectual development will be promoted as she is learning new skills that are needed for her job/she may need to use problem-solving skills when problems arise at work/will need to use her memory and recall to carry out her job
  • Medina's social development will be promoted as she will need to build new relationships/will develop independence
  • Medina may feel more stressed as she is balancing her work with looking after the family.

37. Exam skills 2

1 (a) The ageing process describes the physical changes that take place in later adulthood such as loss of hair, loss of mobility, sensory loss.

(b) Any two from: hair loss; greying hair; loss of muscle tone; loss of strength; loss of mobility; loss of fine motor skills; sensory loss.

(c) Any two from: giving information about her illness; giving medication; giving advice on exercise/diet; reassuring Conrad about her care; coordinating with other services.

38. Exam skills 3

1 (a) Any two from:
  • Malika will feel secure because she has security of income/security of a job
  • Malika will have high self-esteem because she has a good job that has a high status
  • Malika is likely to have a good self-image because she has a responsible job
  • Malika will feel secure because she has a job that she enjoys/is well paid.

(b) Any two from:
  • Ola will lose formal relationships because she is no longer seeing her teachers

  • Ola will have fewer friends because she has dropped out of education where most of her friends will have been
  • Ola may develop a negative self-image because she is not in education or employment
  • Ola's relationship with other members of the family may break down because they may be unhappy about her choice
  • Ola may feel happier/more contented as she is no longer worrying about the course
  • Ola's thinking skills may be affected because she is not learning new things on her course.

39. Exam skills 4

Because Dillon's mother left the family home, the close bonds he had with her may break down because he does not see her every day. Dillon may feel less secure and contented, which may cause him to lose confidence in his own ability. The family breakdown could make it harder for him to build new friendships and relationships because he is worried about being let down again. Dillon may feel that it is his fault that his parents have split up, affecting how he sees himself and giving him a negative self-image. Dillon may feel stressed because his mother has left, which could cause illnesses such as headaches. If Dillon is stressed or unhappy, it is likely to have an effect on his school work as he may have more difficulty concentrating in class. At Dillon's life stage he may be starting puberty, but stress could delay the physical changes that are happening to him. The breakdown could also have a positive effect on the relationship that Dillon has with his dad and help him to develop a much stronger bond with him.

UNIT 9 ANSWERS

LEARNING AIM A

40. Defining health and wellbeing

1 D A complete state of physical, mental and social wellbeing, and not merely the absence of disease or infirmity (Source: WHO, 1948)

2 (a) Any two from:
  • Luisa's physical needs are being met by boxercise and running.
  • Luisa's intellectual needs are being met by working as a teacher.
  • Her emotional needs are being met by seeing her parents and friends regularly.
  • Her social needs are being met by meeting her friends most weekends/mixing with a lot of people at work.

(b) Because all four types of need are being met, Luisa's health and wellbeing are holistic.

3 His physical needs, as he gets hot food and a drink, and his social needs, as he will meet with the volunteers and other homeless people.

41. Physical and intellectual factors

1 1. Eating a balanced diet can lead to weight loss, making it easier to exercise and get fitter.

2. Eating a balanced diet provides the minerals and other nutrients that the brain needs to function efficiently.

2 (a) 1. She has no garden so will not get much fresh air unless she goes for a walk.

2. The house is well looked after, so is likely to be clean and tidy, which means she is less likely to catch germs or have an accident.

(b) 1. She has her own bedroom, so she has somewhere to keep her books and do her homework.

2. As her parents speak Russian at home, Anya is already able to speak two languages fluently, so she often reads books in Russian to improve her language skills.

42. Emotional and social effects

1 1. Drinking too much can result in weight gain, which may result in unhappiness/dissatisfaction.

2. Drinking too much can cause dehydration and headaches, which affects concentration.

2 (a) 1. Will's arthritis means he is in pain most of the time, which could negatively affect his mood if he cannot concentrate on anything else.

2. Will's pain and mobility problems mean that he doesn't get out much. Therefore, he doesn't have many opportunities to see his friends and doesn't have much of a social life.

(b) 1. Will's carers and family visit him regularly, so he has someone to chat to, which distracts him from the pain and cheers him up.

2. Will's carers visit him twice each day and his family visit regularly, so he has social contact with others at least twice every day.

43. Physical effects of an unhealthy lifestyle

1 (a) 1. She will have an increased risk of illness/disease due to the effects of the drugs on her body.

2. She may have a poor diet, resulting in too much weight loss/malnutrition.

(b) 1. Poor living conditions may be cold and damp, so she may be ill more often.

2. She has very little money and spends it on drugs. She is unlikely to spend it on her personal care, so her personal hygiene may be affected.

2 1. Tom's dancing will help his physical fitness by improving his stamina, strength and suppleness, to keep his joints mobile.

2. As a result of his drinking, Tom may put on weight/have an accident because of impaired judgement.

44. Intellectual effects of an unhealthy lifestyle

1 A Reduced success in education
C Poor long-term career prospects

2 (a) 1. He has no company, so he doesn't have anyone to talk to/discuss things with, so he has no mental stimulation.

2. He is unable to get new glasses, so isn't able to read as much.

(b) 1. Zaid would have someone to take him to get new glasses, so he could read and his brain would be stimulated.

2. Zaid would have someone to take him out on trips, so he would see new places and have new experiences.

45. Emotional effects of an unhealthy lifestyle

1 (a) 1. Tanvi is finding it hard to cope emotionally because she is suffering from postnatal depression. This makes her feel likes she is letting Riya down, which makes her upset.

2. Tanvi only has the company of her baby and her grandmother during the day, which makes her feel bored and resentful. She feels guilty that she is feeling this way.

(b) 1. Kim is company for Tanvi and someone for Tanvi to share her concerns with, which reassures her and cheers her up.

2. Kim can provide practical support, such as looking after the baby while Tanvi has a nap or doing some shopping for her, which helps Tanvi to cope and so feel less depressed.

2 1. Sophie is self-conscious about her weight, so she has low self-esteem.

2. Sophie is worried about going to university because she knows she won't join in a lot of the activities, as she is too embarrassed to try them because of her weight.

46. Social effects of an unhealthy lifestyle

1 1. Oscar often eats alone in his room, so he doesn't mix with the other residents, which makes it hard for him to make friends.

2. He only sees his family once a week, so he may feel lonely.

2 (a) Any two from:
- She meets other parents, grandparents and teachers when she collects the children from school, which gives her regular contact with others.
- She doesn't smoke as much because she doesn't want to create a bad impression.
- She enjoys the company and contact with her grandchildren every day.
- She sees their parents every evening when they pick up the children, which gives her regular contact with her family.

(b) 1. She will have been used to doing day-to-day tasks with her husband, such as looking after the house and garden, and shopping.

2. She will miss his company on days out, on holidays and at social events with their friends.

47. Diet and nutrition

1 (a) B Carbohydrate E Protein

(b) 1. Low blood pressure

2. Hair may become thin

2 (a) 1. Weight gain

2. She is more likely to suffer ill health (for example, diabetes)

(b) 1. Jenna could cut down on eating deep-fried food. This would mean she was eating less fat, so her body would use some of the energy she has stored as body fat instead.

2. Jenna could eat a healthy breakfast every day so she was less hungry later in the day. This would mean that she would eat less for her evening meal.

48. Exercise

1 (a) $114/3.35 = 34.0$

(b) D Obese

(c) 1. If Sam did more exercise, he would become physically stronger, with better stamina and suppleness.

2. If Sam did more exercise, he would lose weight, which might make him happier within himself/more confident.

49. Home environment

1 A Increased risk of becoming ill
B More chance of making a health problem worse

2 (a) 1. Chan is unable to get any peace to do her homework, which may affect how well she does at school and therefore her future career prospects.

2. Chan is too embarrassed to invite her friends round. They might think she is being unfriendly and stop asking her to their houses.

(b) 1. Chan's mother always keeps the house clean, so there is less risk of catching illnesses/diseases.

2. Chan's mother and sisters are company for Chan, so she is never lonely and always has someone there to talk to.

50. Work environment

1 1. More stress

2. Less time to spend with family and friends

2 (a) 1. His work environment is very noisy, which may cause long-term damage to his hearing.

2. As he works with his hands using the same tools all day, he has already injured them.

(b) 1. He is doing a skilled job, which gives him a sense of job satisfaction each time his line manager praises his work.

2. He has been at the company a long time and has lots of good friends there, some of whom he enjoys spending time with outside work.

51. Alcohol consumption

1 **B** Men: 21 units / Women: 14 units

2 (a) Binge drinking is drinking heavily in a short space of time to feel the effects of alcohol.

(b) 1. Hannah's judgement may be impaired, so she could potentially put herself into an unsafe situation (for example, unprotected sex).

2. Hannah may develop an alcohol-related illness, such as liver disease, leading to a shortened life expectancy.

3 1. He may have cravings for alcohol.

2. He may suffer withdrawal symptoms, such as anxiety and the shakes.

52. Effects of alcohol

1 (a) 1. Keane might injure himself due to impaired judgement.

2. Keane may not be able to concentrate at work because he has a hangover.

(b) 1. Keane might put on weight.

2. Drinking too much may cause mental health issues, such as hallucinations.

2 1. Her boyfriend could suggest they go to the cinema instead of the bar.

2. Her friends could suggest they sometimes go for a coffee after work instead of for a drink.

53. Smoking

1 **A** Lung cancer **D** Bronchitis

2 (a) 1. Increased blood pressure

2. Hair and clothes smell

(b) Any two from:

• His new friends don't like him smoking and may stop being friends with him if he continues smoking.

• His friends could use positive peer pressure by offering to do some research to find ways he could stop and help him to do so.

• They could find ways to distract him when he wants a cigarette, by suggesting new interests for the group.

• They could encourage him and praise him when he manages to cut down.

54. Recreational drug use

1 (a) She will be more likely to get ill as her immune system is weakened by drug use.

(b) Barbara has been taking drugs for about a year now and enjoys their effects, so she probably won't want to stop. This is part of her social life and even if she tries to stop, she will have temptation put in her way every time she goes out with her new friends. She may have lost contact with her friends from when she was married, as they were friends of her husband, so she may not want to give up her new friends. She likes being part of the group and may worry that she might not be included if she does not join in.

However, she has the support of her family, who are important to her, so she doesn't want them to disapprove of her new friends and lifestyle. She could invite her new friends to do something different and healthier some weekends, such as going to a health spa for a pamper weekend. She could mention to her new friends that she is happy to go clubbing but would rather they didn't offer her drugs any more, as she doesn't like the after-effects on her body the next day. If they are real friends, they will respect that. She could look for other activities to occupy her weekends and give her opportunities to make other friends.

I think that as Barbara is not addicted to drugs and because she doesn't want to disappoint her family, this will give her the motivation to stop taking drugs.

55. Sexual practices

1 **B** Using barrier methods of contraception
   C Taking part in sexual health screening

2 (a) 1. Pregnancy

2. Contracting a sexually transmitted infection (STI)

(b) 1. Sevanna could speak to her doctor.

2. Sevanna could speak to her school nurse.

(c) 1. She will be happy that her partner is treating her with respect.

2. She will not be worried about an unwanted pregnancy or catching an STI.

56. Personal hygiene

1 (a) **B** Changing your clothes once a week

(b) 1. You are less likely to have harmful bacteria or germs on your skin or in other parts of your body, such as your mouth, which means you will be less likely to catch an illness or disease.

2. You will smell fresh, so others will be happy to be around you and be your friend, which will mean that others are happy to socialise with you.

2 Johnny is likely to be embarrassed about sweating so much, which may affect his self-esteem. His work colleagues may be less likely to want to mix with him socially because his personal hygiene is not good. This may mean that he is either withdrawn and on the edge of social groups, or he may be loud and try really hard to be good company, to make up for this.

57. Sleep patterns

1 (a) 1. Good energy levels

2. Improved concentration

(b) One from: shift work can make it hard to sleep at regular times; a noisy workplace to lead to headaches, which can make it hard to sleep; stress can make it hard to get to sleep; an overactive mind can make it hard to sleep.

2 Natalia may not sleep well because the baby may wake her up in the night. Her sleep may also be disturbed by other members of the family because she has a large family and they live in a small house. The house is on a busy road, so she may also be woken up by traffic noises, especially if cars brake suddenly or horns are used. She may also be woken up by people walking home late, for example, from pubs, or by early-morning workers. If her sleep is disturbed she will be tired, so she will find it harder to concentrate on her studies, which may affect her results.

However, Natalia does have her own bedroom. If her room is away from the baby's room and the noise from the street, she should be able to concentrate more. Her parents encourage her to go to bed early, so that she gets enough sleep even if the baby wakes up.

Although her sleep pattern is likely to be disturbed and her studying may not be as effective as it could be if she lived in a different home environment, she should still do quite well, because her parents are supportive of her needs.

58. Influences on lifestyles 1

1 1. The whole family could eat more healthily so Jennifer does not have to cook separate meals for herself or feel she is missing out.
   2. The whole family could go for walks together/do other activities together so that Jennifer is more active and loses weight.

2 1. Rosie may struggle at school because she is often moving on and finds it hard to catch up when she starts a new class. As a result, she may lose interest in learning and may not do as well at school.
   2. She may also miss out on regular visits to the doctor, dentist and optician, as her parents will have to register her with new ones at each place they settle in. As a result, she may miss out on regular health screening.

3 1. Mohammed's diet will not contain pork/alcohol.
   2. Mohammed will believe that it is his role to protect/look after the women in his family, so he may want to work hard to provide for them.

59. Influences on lifestyles 2

1 **D** The influence that people in a particular social group can have on other members of the group

2 (a) 1. As her new friends smoke, Camilla may start to smoke so that she feels accepted in the group.
      2. Camilla may feel she needs to hang out with her older friends when she starts her new school, which may mean that she doesn't make friends with people in her own year group and becomes socially isolated.
   (b) 1. Camilla's new classmates may work hard, which may influence Camilla to focus on her studies to gain good grades.
      2. Camilla's new classmates may not like people who smell of smoke, so they may persuade her to stop smoking so that she is accepted more easily.

60. Influences on lifestyles 3

1 (a) A role model is someone who sets an example and who influences our choices.
   (b) 1. Farrah might have very good manners, so her younger siblings will learn good manners too – for example, being polite to their parents.
      2. Farrah might be praised for keeping her room neat and tidy, so her younger siblings might copy her so they get praised too.

2 (a) 1. The media contains many fashion images, which may influence what Feng wants to wear.
      2. The media may influence what Feng eats. Many images in the media show very slim and attractive females, and this may influence Feng to eat less, to try to be like them.
   (b) 1. Her parents will be role models to Feng. They will influence what she believes in/how she behaves or acts/what she eats or wears/her attitude towards her own and other people's property.
      2. Her teachers will be role models to Feng. They will influence what and how she learns/her attitude towards learning/how she should behave and interact with others.

61. Influences on lifestyles 4

1 **C** The number of holidays taken each year

2 Harry will have to think carefully about the exercise or activities he takes part in. Although he will be able to take part in non-contact sports, such as swimming and badminton, it would be unwise for him to take up contact sports, such as karate or rugby or sports that may have an impact on his body, such as skiing or bungee jumping.

He will also have to think carefully about his career choices as he will need to avoid any job that puts him at risk from injury – for example, manual jobs using sharp tools. A job with flexible working hours will make it easier to fit in his medical appointments.

He should not abuse substances that might lead him to be more careless such as drinking too much or taking recreational drugs as they could impair his judgement and he might make mistakes with his medication or get injured. He will also have to keep a clear head, as he needs to be organised to make sure he has his medication with him at all times and that he takes it when he is supposed to.

His personal hygiene will need to be good as he regularly injects himself, and must avoid catching an infection.

LEARNING AIM B

62. Improving health and wellbeing 1

1 (a) 1. His accommodation
      2. His diet
      3. His exercise
   (b) 1. I intend to move to a dry, warm flat when my current lease runs out.
      2. I intend to eat fewer takeaways and drink fewer energy drinks every day.
      3. I intend to play football for 90 minutes at least twice a week.

2 1. Benefits of meeting targets.
   2. SMART targets.
   3. Strategies to help meet targets.

3 (a) 1. His smoking
      2. His drinking
   (b) He isn't able to change the long distance he has to travel to see his children.

63. Improving health and wellbeing 2

1 **A** Time commitment **D** Getting started

2 1. Mike may find it hard to motivate himself to start a fitness plan when he knows he cannot play for at least six months, which may seem a long way off.
   2. Mike is likely to find it hard to access professional help, as there may not be enough money for the club to have extra trainers or a physiotherapist to help injured players.

3 1. Hui might be demotivated without his wife's support.

2. He might say he has put on so much weight that the problem is too big to tackle, so he might as well not bother starting.

64. Improving health and wellbeing 3

1 It is easy to put off getting started on a health improvement plan if time isn't set aside. If you run out of time, it is easy to put off starting until the next day or week. You may need to get up earlier to make the time.

2 1. Davinder could get up an hour earlier on the days he runs, to allow him time to stretch, run and shower.

2. Davinder could arrange to meet a friend to run instead of meeting him for a drink, to make sure he finds time and doesn't make excuses.

3 1. She could buy herself rewards, such as a new top, with the money she has saved from not drinking alcohol.

2. She could have a list of benefits, such as a better time for her half-marathon, which she could read when her motivation dips.

65. Improving health and wellbeing 4

1 (a) **D** Specific, Measurable, Achievable, Realistic, Time-related

(b) **D** Run for 30 minutes every Saturday and Wednesday and cycle to work three days a week

2 (a) 1. Lose 1.5 kg in the first week.

2. Lose 1 kg a week after the first week until the target weight is reached.

(b) Weigh herself every week and, if she is more than 1.5 kg over her goal weight, go back on a diet.

3 (a) 1. Only eat one fast food meal a week.

2. Eat five portions of fruit and vegetables a day.

3. Walk briskly to school every day instead of catching the bus.

4. Improve his score in the beep test by at least one level every time he does it for the next five weeks.

66. Improving health and wellbeing 5

1 (a) 1. Short-term: Drink alcohol very other day

2. Medium-term: Drink alcohol twice a week and only at weekends (for example, with a meal at the weekend)

(b) 1. Short-term: Fewer headaches/hangovers in the morning

2. Short-term: Increased concentration

3. Long-term: Weight loss

4. Long-term: Money saved

2 (a) 1. They could write down what they drink and how much alcohol they drink, and work out how many units they have consumed in one night. This will hopefully make them realise how many units they are drinking in a week and the damage they may be doing to their health.

2. They could go for a walk after their evening meal, which will mean they are doing something other than drinking alcohol. It will also mean that they get more exercise, which will help with their weight loss.

(b) 1. They may get bored with the existing strategies, so instead they could reward themselves (for example, buy themselves something new, such as a book, if they cut down by a certain amount each week).

2. If the weather is really bad and they don't want to go outside, they could go to bed earlier and read a book, to spend the time doing something else.

67. Improving health and wellbeing 6

1 **B** The use of the power of suggestion to help overcome a problem

2 1. Fine needles are inserted into the skin at certain points on the body.

2. The needles stimulate points in the body to correct energy imbalances and help illness.

3 1. Tao could write down how he would feel if someone had been stealing from him/how the people he is stealing from would feel if they found out what he had been doing. Thinking about this will hopefully make him feel ashamed and stop him doing this again.

2. Tao could write a list of pros and cons of giving up. Seeing the cons on paper may scare him into becoming more determined to give up.

3. Tao could work out how much money he spends on drugs in a month and what he could buy with that money instead. This should hopefully make him realise how much money he is wasting.

68. Formal support

1 (a) Formal support is support provided by someone who has been trained and who is usually paid.

(b) 1. Teacher

2. Counsellor

2 1. He could ask a female doctor or a practice nurse to have a chat with her to make sure she gets advice and doesn't go away and have unsafe sex.

2. He could refer her to a formal support group, such as Brook, which specialises in this area so knows how best to talk to adolescent girls about the subject.

3 1. Doctor

2. Dietician

3. A slimming club

69. Informal support

1 (a) 1. Her family provides practical support by helping with her shopping and giving love/company.

2. Her friends provide her with conversation/company/an opportunity to talk about shared memories.

(b) 1. They could give her lifts to appointments with the doctor/optician.

2. They could help her read her post and deal with it (for example, help her pay her bills).

3. They could reassure her/comfort her when she gets frustrated that she can't do as much for herself as she used to.

4. They could take her out to visit friends/new places so she still has opportunities to meet other people.

70. Support in maintaining positive change

1 **C** Criticism

2 (a) She may give up as her diet doesn't seem to be working and because the problem seems to be too big to solve (that is, she still has a lot of weight to lose).

(b) Any two from:

- They could persuade her to stick to her plan by explaining to her that it is common for progress to slow down.
- They could provide ongoing support by giving her short-term targets each week and encouragement to meet them/praise when she reaches them.

- They could remind her why she started the diet in the first place and the long-term benefits of losing weight.

3 1. An organisation that supports smokers who are giving up could provide suggestions for alternative things to have when he has a craving (for example, eating a healthy snack) or alternative therapies (for example, nicotine patches).

   2. He could ask his work colleagues who don't smoke to distract him in some way (for example, by going for a coffee instead).

71. Barriers to health 1

1 (a) 1. George can no longer afford to pay for sessions with his personal trainer, which means he is less likely to find the time and the motivation to get fitter.

       2. George will find it harder to find time to commit to fitness, because his wife may need more help during her pregnancy/he will be more tired when the new baby arrives.

   (b) 1. He needs to write down when he is going to do the exercises that his trainer taught him each day, with a list of benefits, so he is motivated to try to keep doing them on his own.

       2. He could do some exercise at lunchtime instead of chatting to his colleagues, maybe asking them to join him, so it does not impact on his time at home.

2 1. Perry's learning difficulties have meant that he is easily persuaded to do things to be liked and accepted as part of a group.

   2. Perry was unable to access the school nurse when he was worried about starting smoking, so went ahead without any advice and guidance in school. He is therefore unlikely to try to access the nurse to ask for help with stopping smoking.

72. Barriers to health 2

1 (a) 1. Clare cannot go for a walk on her own during the day because she needs someone with her and her partner is at work/her friends are at work. She therefore isn't able to get any exercise to help with her weight loss.

       2. Clare's friends bring her chocolates, which puts temptation in her way. Her reduced mobility will mean that if she eats these and doesn't exercise, she is likely to put on weight.

   (b) Any two from:
   - Clare could do some exercises sitting down, such as arm exercises.
   - She could walk around the ground floor of the house to get some exercise.
   - She will have been given exercises to strengthen her knee and she could do these with both legs to get some exercise.
   - She could ask her friends to bring her flowers, books or magazines instead of chocolates, to avoid temptation.

2 1. The media portrays images of very slim models.

   2. Her mother gives her junk food.

73. Barriers to health 3

1 1. Low self-esteem

   2. A lack of motivation

2 Nigel will find it very hard to motivate himself to recover, as he has such a big task ahead of him and he will only see very small changes each week. Although he will have a physiotherapist on hand to work with him every day in hospital, he will find it harder when he leaves hospital, as that support won't be immediately on hand. He may end up feeling bored, resentful and unhappy, as he is no longer able to get out and do the things he used to, such as running, playing football or going to work. Not being able to get out as easily may mean he becomes socially isolated.

However, Nigel may decide that he doesn't want to be beaten by this setback. He will still be able to use gym equipment such as a cycling machine, and do exercises to strengthen his left leg and arm and keep his right leg and arm in top condition. He can retrain for a different job and learn new skills and meet new people. He can find new interests and hobbies, such as reading, the theatre and quizzes, so keep his mind active. He will also meet new people, some with similar disabilities, in the rehab unit or at a support group when he leaves hospital.

If Nigel adopts a positive attitude, he is likely to achieve a healthy lifestyle again. It will be different from his previous lifestyle, but it could be just as rewarding.

74. Barriers to health 4

1 In order to adopt a healthy lifestyle, Magnus will need help. He could seek help from one of the charities that help homeless people and get a few nights sleeping in a shelter, so that he can get cleaned up and start planning his new future. He could then find out about any benefits he is entitled to while he looks for a job, so that he has enough money to rent a room somewhere. Once he has a job and some money coming in, he can start to eat more healthily/ get fitter (and look to stop smoking). In his new job, he will learn new skills, meet new people and make new friends.

However, Magnus may find it hard to find a job, especially because of his previous employment history. He is also likely to be rejected by some employers, which may make him feel like he will never be accepted. He might be tempted to give up and go back to his old ways. The rejection by his parents will have been painful and he may find it hard to get in touch with them again, fearing more rejection.

If Magnus is determined enough, there is enough help and support available to help him get off the streets and into a position where he can adopt a healthy lifestyle.

75. Exam skills 1

1 45/2.56 = 17.6

2 120/4.41 = 27.2

76. Exam skills 2

1 **A** Underweight

2 **C** Overweight

77. Exam skills 3

1 Liver disease

2 1. Jasmine's friends could arrange to go for a walk every week in the park. During the walk, they could plan what they are going to do that evening. If Jasmine doesn't go for the walk, she won't find out what they are up to and won't be able to go out with them.

   2. Jasmine's friends could all go on a diet to raise money for charity and persuade her to join in. They could all meet to weigh one another every week. As they would be dieting to raise money for charity, she may feel guilty if she doesn't take part.

3   Colin will have company in the form of care home staff/
    other residents, so he will always have someone to talk to.

78. Exam skills 4

1   Shirley has a busy job. She may find it hard to give up her
    wine each evening as it helps her to feel relaxed at the end
    of her marking and preparation. She may not understand
    why she is overweight, as she exercises every week and may
    wonder why she is bothering to do it. She may also find it
    hard to give up eating out as she enjoys this and it is part of
    her social life. One of the pleasures of going to the holiday
    cottage is eating out to give her a break from cooking.

    However, Shirley is an intelligent person and knows what
    she needs to do to help herself. Instead of having a couple
    of glasses of wine to relax every night, she could have a
    long soak in the bath/an early night with her book and
    she could still have one glass of wine every other night, as
    alcohol in moderation is beneficial to health. She could pay
    for a session with a personal trainer at the gym so she can
    get advice on how to change her exercise routine to increase
    her heart rate and burn off more calories. She could look
    for alternative treats to eating out, such as going to the
    theatre or cinema or to a museum, and eat a healthy meal at
    home before going out.

    Overall, Shirley has a good chance of achieving her goal
    if she thinks about the possible long-term effects of high
    blood pressure on her health. This will motivate her to keep
    going.

79. Unit 1: Practice assessment test

1 (a) Brian: Early adulthood
        Marc: Adolescence

   (b) **B** Intellectual development

   (c) An emotional bond between a parent and child

   (d) (i) and (ii)

Intellectual skill	Activity
Language	Puppet play
	Picture books
Memory	Action rhymes
	Hide and seek with a toy

   (e) Any two from: talking to friends will increase Kate's
        vocabulary; she will learn to share/take turns; she
        will develop friendships/develop a special friendship;
        she will develop confidence; she will develop
        independence.

   (f) Any two from: he is likely to feel good about himself/
        have a positive self-image; he is likely to have high
        self-esteem; he may feel contented with his life/
        achievements.

   (g) Any two from: testes enlarge and produce sperm;
        prostate gland produces secretions; penis enlarges;
        growth spurts; growth of facial hair; growth of hair
        in armpits; growth of pubic hair; voice box (larynx)
        grows so the voice deepens (breaks).

   (h) (i) Any two from: Liz may feel stressed and anxious
             because she is concerned that Ross will miss her
             and not be happy with his aunt; Liz may feel
             guilty because she is worried that the children will
             be unhappy/will not cope without her; Liz may be
             worried about her health because she is not sure
             that the operation will improve her back problems;
             Liz's mobility/gross motor skills may be affected
             because she has had an operation on her back,
             which may take time to heal.

        (ii) **Positive:**
             One from: Ross will begin to develop relationships
             with someone other than his parents; he may
             become more independent when he is with his
             aunt, because he cannot rely on his mother for his
             needs; he will learn how to cope/come to terms
             with his feelings because he does not have his
             mother there to comfort him.

             Negative:
             One from: Ross may be unhappy and show anxiety
             because his mother isn't there to comfort him; the
             strong attachment that Ross had with his mother
             may break down because he has been separated
             from her for some time; his ability to form
             relationships may be affected in the future because
             of the stress and anxiety he is experiencing.

2 (a) (i) **Expected life event:**
             One from: going to school, college or university;
             getting a job; getting married.

             Unexpected life event:
             One from: being promoted; getting divorced.

        (ii) Any two from: he could become stressed due to
             distress over his relationship break-up; he may
             not bother about his appearance and wellbeing;
             he may adopt an unhealthy lifestyle (for example,
             start smoking, drink alcohol excessively or eat
             unhealthily); he may experience reduced energy/
             motivation due to his relationship break-up; he
             may become unable to function at work due to
             anxiety about the relationship break-up; stress
             may affect his attitudes/relationship with Micha;
             he may develop a negative self-image because he
             feels rejected.

        (iii) Any two from: it will strengthen his muscles and
             joints; it will improve his mobility and stamina;
             it will improve his mood/help to create a positive
             self-image.

   (b) (i) Any two from: give information and advice about
             the condition; give emotional support to Rafal
             by listening/answering questions; give advice on
             training and employment; direct Rafal and Micha
             to other services.

        (ii) Any two from: his growth and physiological
             change may be delayed because of health
             conditions relating to Down's syndrome; his
             disability will affect the progress of his learning
             because he will have more difficulty with
             memory and developing abstract thought; he
             may experience discrimination and negative
             comments because of his condition, which may
             affect the way he sees himself/his self-image;
             he may become upset and anxious because
             he may experience health conditions, such as
             digestive or heart problems; the condition may
             affect his independence and opportunities for
             socialising/building friendships, because he still
             needs the support from others and isn't able to
             go out independently; his condition may affect
             opportunities to develop intimate relationships/a
             partnership with another person, as he may not be
             accepted by them.

        (iii) Any two from: Rafal may feel guilty because his
             son's disorder is an inherited condition, so it has
             been passed down from him and Lena; Rafal
             may feel anxious/worried about Micha's health
             because the condition can cause other health

problems (for example, problems with the heart and digestive system); Rafal may feel happy/secure because his son lives with him and they have a close relationship; Rafal may be worried about Micha's future life because he may have difficulty in getting a job/earning money; Rafal may feel stressed and concerned that he may not be meeting Micha's care needs; caring for Micha may have an effect on Rafal's ability to develop relationships, because he has less time to go out and socialise.

(c) Any two from: he may develop an improved self-image because he is proud of his partner; he may feel more secure now that he is in a relationship and has someone to share his interests with/someone to socialise with; he may be more contented because he is in a secure relationship with Maia; he may have an improved state of health and wellbeing because he is feeling more contented with his life.

(d) During the holiday, Micha will be learning new practical skills, such as cooking and cleaning, which will help him to become more independent when he goes home.

Micha will need to develop thinking skills and memory when taking part in sailing to help him with the handling of the boat. This will give him a sense of achievement and improve his self-esteem. Being away from Rafal for the first time will improve his confidence to be independent, which help to further improve his self-esteem and provide a positive self-image. However, Micha may feel distressed about being away from Rafal. If he has any difficulties with his peers he may develop a negative self-image.

While Micha is away, Rafal will have more time to himself for socialising and also for developing his relationship with Maia.

Rafal is likely to be happy that Micha has been given a holiday, which will improve his own feeling of wellbeing and contentment.

Overall, the holiday will be a positive experience for both Micha and Rafal.

85. Unit 9: Practice assessment test

1 (a) 1. Possibility of catching an illness or disease
   2. Body odour

   (b) An obese person may sweat more with exertion, and so will not smell very pleasant. They may also have places on their bodies, such as below the stomach, where sweat can cause skin infections and add to the body odour.

2 (a) **B** Fatigue **C** Accidents
   (b) High blood pressure

3 (a) **D** Regularly leaving work on time to spend time with family and friends
   (b) 1. A good work/life balance means a person has time to spend with their family and friends.
   2. A good work/life balance means that the person will be less stressed and so live a longer, more healthy life.

4 (a) 1. Maintain a healthy weight
   2. Higher energy levels

5 His friends could ask him to stay in school with them so they can eat a quick healthy lunch together and then have the time to go to a school activity, such as the badminton club.

6 (a) $\text{BMI} = \dfrac{58}{1.8^2}$

   $\text{BMI} = 17.9\,\text{kg/m}^2$

   (b) **A** Underweight

7 1. Eating a healthy diet means your brain receives the correct nutrients it needs to be alert and active.
   2. Not becoming addicted to anything, such as cigarettes, alcohol, drugs or food, means you are not distracted by cravings and so are better able to concentrate.

8 1. Taking drugs can lead to health risks such as contracting diseases – for example, HIV or AIDS through sharing needles.
   2. Taking drugs can lead to taking careless risks, due to hallucinations such as thinking you can fly, and so can lead to accidents and even death.

9 (a) 1. Lower risk of cardiovascular disease
   2. Decreased risk of dementia

   (b) 1. Alcohol contains calories, so drinking too much can lead to weight gain.
   2. Drinking too much can lead to addiction and mood changes, which can eventually lead to mental health issues.

   (c) 1. Support groups such as AA (Alcoholics Anonymous).
   2. Your GP can refer you for counselling.

10 1. Richard has smoked for so long that he automatically reaches for a cigarette many times a day. He is addicted to nicotine so he may find the cravings for a cigarette really hard to resist, feel that it is an impossible task and not really start.
   2. Richard has a stressful job and feels he needs the cigarettes to relieve some of the stress.

11 1. Living on the ninth floor means that Carmel has no garden to play in and the windows will be kept closed so she doesn't fall out, so she may not get much fresh air or exercise.
   2. They have a limited income, so Nicky may cook Carmel cheap meals such as egg and chips, so Carmel will not be eating a balanced diet.

12 Lance will still worry that he may have a heart attack and so be stressed. He will also find it harder to exercise due to his excess weight, so may give up. He will find it hard to diet and give up alcohol because he enjoys his food and drink. He has also got out of the habit of exercising.

However, if he listens to his doctor and starts by dieting and cutting down on alcohol, he will lose weight. This will cause less strain on his heart which, along with the information from his doctor, will reassure him and help him get over his fear. As he does more exercise, the thought of being able to take up his interests again will help to motivate him.

I think that the risks to his health of being overweight and his memories of how good he felt when he was fit and active will motivate him enough to achieve his goal of becoming fit again.